SCIENCE

Curriculum Bank

KEY STAGE TWO
SCOTTISH LEVELS C-E

LIFE PROCESSES AND LIVING THINGS

FRANCES MACKAY

Published by Scholastic Ltd,
Villiers House,
Clarendon Avenue,
Leamington Spa,
Warwickshire CV32 5PR
Text © 1995 Frances Mackay
© 1995 Scholastic Ltd
1 2 3 4

AUTHOR
FRANCES MACKAY

EDITOR
NOEL PRITCHARD

ASSISTANT EDITOR
JOEL LANE

SERIES DESIGNER
LYNNE JOESBURY

DESIGNER
ANNA OLIWA

ILLUSTRATIONS
MAGGIE DOWNER

COVER ILLUSTRATION
JONATHAN BENTLEY

INFORMATION TECHNOLOGY CONSULTANT
MARTIN BLOWS

SCOTTISH 5–14 LINKS
MARGARET SCOTT AND SUSAN GOW

Designed using Aldus Pagemaker

British Library Cataloguing-in-Publication Data
A catalogue record for this book is available from the British
Library.

ISBN 0-590-53370-3

Contents

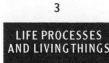

LIFE PROCESSES
AND LIVING THINGS

Introduction

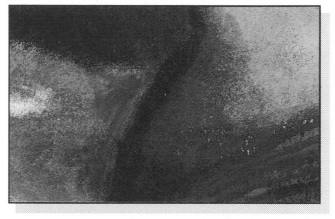

Scholastic Curriculum Bank is a series for all primary teachers, providing an essential planning tool for devising comprehensive schemes of work as well as an easily accessible and varied bank of practical, classroom-tested activities with photocopiable resources.

Designed to help planning for and implementation of progression, differentiation and assessment, *Scholastic Curriculum Bank* offers a structured range of stimulating activities with clearly-stated learning objectives that reflect the programmes of study, and detailed lesson plans that allow busy teachers to put ideas into practice with the minimum amount of preparation time. The photocopiable sheets that accompany many of the activities provide ways of integrating purposeful application of knowledge and skills, differentiation, assessment and record-keeping.

Opportunities for formative assessment are highlighted where appropriate within the activities, while separate summative assessment activities give guidelines for analysis and subsequent action. Ways of using information technology for different purposes and within different contexts, as a tool for communicating and handling information and as a method for investigating, are integrated into the activities where appropriate, and more explicit guidance is provided at the end of the book.

The series covers all the primary curriculum subjects with separate books for Key Stages 1 and 2 or Scottish Levels A–B and C–E. It can be used as a flexible resource with any scheme, to fulfil National Curriculum and Scottish 5–14 requirements and to provide children with a variety of different learning experiences that will lead to effective acquisition of skills and knowledge.

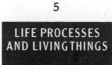

LIFE PROCESSES
AND LIVING THINGS

SCHOLASTIC CURRICULUM BANK SCIENCE

The *Scholastic Curriculum Bank Science* books enable teachers to plan comprehensive and structured coverage of the primary science curriculum and pupils to develop the required skills, knowledge and understanding through activities that promote scientific thinking and ways of working.

Each book covers one key stage. At Key Stage 1/Scottish levels A–B, all areas of science are covered in one book. At Key Stage 2, there are three books which reflect the sections of the programme of study (Life Processes and Living Things, Materials and their Properties and Physical Processes). Experimental and Investigative science is integrated into the three Key Stage 2/Scottish levels C–E books, so that it is tackled in context.

Bank of activities

This book provides a bank of activities that can be used in many different ways – to form a framework for a scheme of work; to add breadth and variety to an existing scheme; or to supplement a particular topic. The activities are designed to address a number of important areas of study.

Systematic enquiry

A wide range of activities has been presented, to create opportunities for focused exploration and investigation to acquire scientific knowledge, understanding and skills. The

activities involve both firsthand experience and the use of other sources of information. Opportunities for the use of IT for storing, retrieving and presenting information, and for investigative purposes, are suggested throughout.

Communication skills

The activities aim to develop children's communication skills by encouraging them to:
▲ ask questions;
▲ learn and use scientific vocabulary;
▲ use standard measures;
▲ discuss findings with others;
▲ present data in a variety of different ways.

Science in everyday life

Through a variety of domestic and environmental contexts, pupils are able to acquire an awareness of the importance of science in everyday life, of the part science has played in the development of many of the things they use, and of the need to treat their environment with care and sensitivity.

The nature of scientific ideas

The activities will help children to understand that scientific knowledge and understanding rely on evidence, and that scientific evidence can be obtained in a number of ways. They will also help children to realise that science can provide explanations for many of the things that happen around them.

Health and safety

The activities encourage children to develop their knowledge and understanding of health and safety when working with living things and with materials. They will help pupils to recognise potential hazards to themselves and others, assess the risks to themselves and others, and take action to help control the risks.

Lesson plans

Detailed lesson plans, under clear headings, are given for each activity and provide material for immediate implementation in the classroom. The structure for each activity is as follows:

Activity title box

The information contained in the box at the beginning of each activity outlines the following key aspects:

▲ *Activity title and learning objective* – For each activity, a clearly-stated learning objective is given in bold italics. These learning objectives break down aspects of the programmes of study into manageable, hierarchical teaching and learning chunks, and their purpose is to aid planning for progression. These objectives can be easily referenced to the National Curriculum and Scottish 5–14 requirements by using the overview grids at the end of this chapter (pages 9 to 12).

▲ *Class organisation/Likely duration* – Icons †† and ⊕ signpost the suggested group sizes for each activity and the approximate amount of time required to complete it.

▲ *Safety* – Where necessary, safety considerations are flagged with the ⚠ icon.

Previous skills/knowledge needed

Information is given here when it is necessary for the children to have acquired specific knowledge or skills prior to carrying out the activity.

Key background information

The information in this section is intended to help the teacher to understand the scientific concepts and ideas covered in each activity. It generally goes beyond the level of understanding expected of most children, but will help to give the teacher confidence to ask and answer questions and to guide the children in their investigations.

Preparation

Advice is given for those occasions where it is necessary for the teacher to prime the pupils for the activity or to prepare materials, or to set up a display or activity ahead of time.

Resources needed

All of the materials needed to carry out the activity are listed, so that either the pupils or the teacher can gather them together easily before the beginning of the teaching session.

What to do

Easy-to-follow, step-by-step instructions are given for carrying out the activity, including (where appropriate) suggested questions for the teacher to ask the pupils to help instigate discussion and stimulate investigation.

Suggestion(s) for extension/support

Ideas are given for ways of providing for easy differentiation where activities lend themselves to this purpose. In all cases, suggestions are provided as to how each activity can be modified for the less able or extended for the more able.

Assessment opportunities

Where appropriate, opportunities for ongoing assessment by the teacher during or after a specific activity are highlighted.

Opportunities for IT

Where opportunities for IT present themselves, these are briefly outlined with reference to particularly suitable types of program. The chart on page 158 presents specific areas of IT covered in the activities, together with more detailed support on how to apply particular types of program. Selected lesson plans serve as models for other activities by providing more comprehensive guidance on the application of IT, and these are indicated by the bold page numbers on the grid and the 🖳 icon at the start of an activity.

Display ideas

Where they are relevant and innovative, display ideas are incorporated into activity plans and illustrated with examples.

Other aspects of the Science PoS covered

Inevitably, activities will cover aspects of the programmes of study in other areas of the science curriculum; and in particular, Experimental and Investigative Science will be a feature of many of them. These links are highlighted under this heading.

Reference to photocopiable sheets

Where activities include photocopiable activity sheets, small reproductions of these are included in the lesson plans, together with guidance notes for their use and, where appropriate, suggested answers.

Investigations

Although aspects of Experimental and Investigative Science will be integral to most activities, each book includes a separate section of investigations and real-life problem-solving activities. These activities are more open-ended than those elsewhere in the book, and provide opportunities to test ideas and carry out whole investigations, utilising and building on content knowledge. Guidance for the teacher on concepts likely to emerge from such investigations is given. Activities suitable for investigations are flagged by the ⚘ icon.

Assessment

This chapter provides a range of tasks related to the main areas of study covered elsewhere in the book that can be used for summative assessment purposes. The activities have been designed so that they can either be used as individual tasks to provide the teacher with an ongoing evaluation of the children's progress or, alternatively, be presented together as a form of summative assessment at the end of a whole unit or at the end of Key Stage 2. The worksheets that make up the tasks can be found at the end of the Photocopiable section (pages 139 to 157). Activities intended for assessment purposes are flagged by the ✐ icon.

Photocopiable activity sheets

Many of the activities are accompanied by photocopiable activity sheets. There may be more than one version of some activities; or an activity sheet may be 'generic', with a facility for the teacher to fill in the appropriate task in order to provide differentiation by task. Other sheets may be more open-ended, to provide differentiation by outcome.

Cross-curricular links

Cross-curricular links are identified on a simple grid which cross-references the particular areas of study in science to the programmes of study for other subjects in the curriculum, and where appropriate provides suggestions for activities. (See page 160.)

LIFE PROCESSES AND LIVING THINGS

The study of living things has always held a fascination for children. This book aims to harness that fascination and develop it further through interesting, relevant and purposeful science activities.

A study of living things will provide children with opportunities to develop their natural curiosity about the world around them, and to make comparisons between themselves and the lives of the plants and animals which share our environment. Teaching children how to care for plants and animals will help them to develop a sense of responsibility towards living things, and will pave the way for more in-depth studies of the complex relationships and interdependencies that exist.

The study of living things offers a range of opportunities for practical investigations which involve firsthand experience of nature, and which will help children to develop skills in observation, identification, classification and recording. Activities which require a closer examination of the human organism will stimulate interest in the classroom, since all children are keen to find out more about themselves and how their bodies work.

This book aims to develop the children's knowledge and understanding of life processes and living things through a wide variety of scientific activities, designed to cater for the broad range of abilities and interests in the primary classroom. Overall, the book aims to provide the teacher with the full amount of support and encouragement needed to teach children about living things. All that needs to be supplied is curiosity and enthusiasm – qualities that the children will (hopefully) possess already.

Learning objective	PoS/AO	Content	Type of activity	Page
Living things and their environment				
Things are living or non-living.	1a (KS1)/*Living Things and the Processes of Life: Variety and Characteristics of Living Things, Level B*	Sorting things into living and non-living. Agreeing on a list of characteristics.	Pair or group sorting and discussion. Whole-class discussion.	14
Many living things have common characteristics.	1a (KS1)/*as above, Level B*	Observation of plants and animals. Finding similarities.	Pair or group observations. Recording. Whole-class discussion.	15
All animals move.	1a/*Processes of Life, Level B*	Observation of minibeasts. Setting up an investigation into how minibeasts move.	Individual or group observation. Recording. Group investigation.	16
All animals feed.	1a/*as above, Level B*	Finding out what animals eat. Collating information using IT. Observation of birds or minibeasts feeding.	Paired research using reference material. Use of IT program (data handling). Group observations. Investigations.	18
All animals breathe.	1a/*as above, Level B*	Discussion about the different breathing mechanisms in animals – lungs, gills, tracheae. Observation of breathing in fish or small mammals.	Teacher-directed, whole-class lesson and discussion. Individual or paired observation.	19
All animals grow and reproduce.	1a/*as above, Level B*	Finding out about animal life cycles. Observation of mealworms or tadpoles.	Individual sorting activity. Small-group research. Whole-class discussion. Small-group observation, daily diary.	21
Living things can be sorted into groups.	4b (KS1)/*as above, Level B*	Sorting things into groups – collection of everyday objects, assortment of plants, pictures of animals.	Small-group sorting. Whole-class discussion.	23
Keys can be used to classify living things.	4a/*as above, Level C*	Sorting pictures of minibeasts using a key. Making a key.	Individuals or pairs. Teacher-directed whole-class discussion.	24
Keys can help to identify living things in the local environment.	4a/*as above, Level C*	Identifying plants and minibeasts in the local environment using a key. Collecting leaves and seeds to make a key.	Whole-class activity working in pairs or small groups. Individuals or pairs designing own key.	26
Different plants and animals are found in different habitats.	5a/*Interaction of Living Things with their Environment, Level C*	Visiting 4 different sites to compare the plants and animals found there. Using keys and reference books.	Small groups, observation in local area. Recording.	28
Plants are suited to their environment.	5b/*as above, Level C*	Visiting 2 different sites to observe how living things adapt to their habitat.	Whole-class activity, working in pairs. Whole-class discussion.	30
Animals are suited to their environment.	5b/*as above, Level C*	Finding out how water and land animals are suited to their environments.	Pairs. Use of reference books. Whole-class discussion.	31
Plants and animals depend on each other.	5b/*as above, Level C*	Finding out how plants and animals can help each other.	Individuals or pairs. Use of reference books. Whole-class discussion.	33

LIFE PROCESSES AND LIVING THINGS

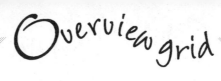

Learning objective	PoS/AO	Content	Type of activity	Page
Food chains show feeding relationships between living things.	5c/as above, Level C	Finding out about food chains in a pond.	Individuals or pairs. Use of reference books. Whole-class discussion.	34
Nearly all food chains start with green plants.	5d/as above, Level C	A game making food webs which all begin with a plant.	Whole-class game.	36
Micro-organisms can be beneficial or harmful.	5e/as above, Level C	Investigation of food decomposition. Finding out about germs.	Group investigation. Use of recording. Observation. Whole-class discussion.	37
Plants				
There is a huge variety of different plants.	5a (KS1)/Variety and Characteristics of Living Things, Level B	Going on a walk to observe and collect plant specimens.	Pairs or small groups. Group sharing of what was found on the walk.	40
Plants can be sorted into groups.	4b (KS1)/as above, Level B	Using and sorting potted plants. Looking for similarities and differences.	Whole-class activity and discussion.	41
Keys can be used to classify plants.	4a/as above, Level C	Using two different keys to identify tree leaves. Using a leaf collection for sorting. Making a key.	Pairs or small groups. Using keys.	42
Plants need water to grow.	3a/Interaction of Living Things with their Environment, Level B	Investigation into how much water is needed for growth of bean seedlings.	Pairs or small groups. Investigation. Recording. Whole-class discussion.	44
Plants need sunlight to grow.	3a/as above, Level B	Investigation of bean seedlings to observe how the amount of light affects growth.	Pairs or small groups. Investigation. Recording. Whole-class discussion.	45
Plants need nutrients to grow.	1b/as above, Level B	Investigation of growing mediums for bean seedlings.	Pairs or small groups. Investigation. Recording. Whole-class discussion.	47
Temperature affects plant growth.	3a/as above, Level B	Investigation of how temperature affects bean seed germination.	Pairs or small groups. Investigation. Recording. Whole-class discussion.	49
Plants are capable of movement.	1b/as above, Level B	Investigation of how cress seeds move in response to a light source.	Pairs or small groups. Investigation. Recording. Whole-class discussion.	50
The root has a particular function in plants.	3c/The Processes of Life, Level B	Observation of roots. Growing plants to observe roots.	Small groups. Observation. Teacher-directed lesson about root function. Recording.	51
The stem has a particular function in plants.	3c/as above, Level B	Observation of stems. Observation of coloured water travelling to other plant parts in flowers.	Pairs or small groups. Investigation/observation. Whole-class discussion. Teacher-directed lesson about stem function.	52
The leaves have a particular function in plants.	3b/as above, Level B	Observation of leaves on potted plants and in a leaf collection. Discussion about photosynthesis. Investigation into transpiration.	Small groups. Observation. Teacher-directed lesson about leaf function. Investigation.	54

LIFE PROCESSES
AND LIVING THINGS

Learning objective	PoS/AO	Content	Type of activity	Page
Green plants are able to make their own food.	3b/*as above, Level D*	Discussion about photosynthesis. Testing for starch in leaves.	Small groups. Teacher-led discussion. Experiment. Whole-class discussion.	56
The flower has a particular function in plants.	3d/*as above, Level D*	Observation of flowers. Discussion about pollination, seed production, fertilisation.	Small groups. Teacher-led discussion. Observation.	57
Plants can be propagated in a variety of ways.	1b/*as above, Level C*	Growing plants in a variety of ways – plantlets, cuttings, offsets, dividing, from leaves, from seeds.	Small groups. Experiment. Observation. Recording.	58
Plants disperse their seeds in a variety of ways.	3d/*as above, Level B*	Observation of seeds. Study of how dandelion seeds fall. Making a model dandelion parachute.	Small groups. Observation. Investigation. Whole-class discussion.	60
Flowering plants have a life cycle.	3d/*as above, Level B*	Putting pictures in correct order to show life cycle.	Whole class. Whole-class discussion. Use of reference books.	61
Ourselves				
There are similarities between humans.	4a (KS1)/*Living Things and the Processes of Life: Variety and Characteristics of Living Things, Level A*	Discussion about things humans have in common. Survey of own family.	Whole class or small groups. Group discussion. Survey.	64
There are differences between humans.	4b (KS1)/*as above, Level A*	Discussing differences between people (including differences between self and other pupils).	Small groups. Measuring, recording. Class discussion.	65
Humans grow and change.	2g/*as above, Level A*	Measuring changes in the body over several months.	Small groups or pairs. Measurement, recording, graphing. Whole-class discussion.	67
Humans need food and water for activity and growth	2b/*Processes of Life, Level B*	Keeping a food diary for one week. Discussion about why we need to eat and drink.	Whole class. Recording. Whole-class discussion.	68
A varied diety is needed to stay healthy.	2b/*Health: Looking after oneself, Level B*	Discussion about types and amounts of food needed to stay healthy. Planning healthy meals.	Whole class. Discussion. Planning menus.	70
Teeth have particular functions.	2a/*as above, Level B*	Discussion about functions and names of teeth. Looking at own teeth – shape, number, how they chew.	Small groups. Discussion. Observation. Recording.	71
Teeth need special care.	2a/*as above, Level A*	Discussion about caring for teeth. Showing how to brush teeth. Writing about ways to care for teeth.	Small groups. Discussion. Observation. Writing about dental care.	72
The skeleton provides support for the body.	2f/*Living Things and the Processes of Life: Processes of Life, Level B*	Discussing bone names and functions. Measuring bones in the body.	Pairs. Whole-class discussion. Measuring. Recording.	74

LIFE PROCESSES
AND LIVINGTHINGS

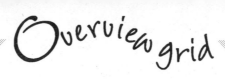
Learning objective	PoS/AO	Content	Type of activity	Page
Joints allow movement of the skeleton.	2f/as above, Level B	Discussion about types and names of joints, how the body can move. Making model ball and socket and hinge joints.	Whole class or small groups. Discussion. Following instructions.	75
Muscles allow body movement.	2f/as above, Level B	Discussion about muscles. Observation. Measurement of muscles.	Whole class. Discussion. Measurement, recording.	76
The heart pumps blood throughout the body.	2c, 2d/as above, Level C	Discussion about heart structure and blood vessels. Making a model heart valve.	Whole class, then pairs. Discussion. Following instructions, making a model.	78
The pulse rate changes with exercise.	2e/Interaction of Living Things with their Environment, Level C	Discussion about our pulse, what it is, finding it. Investigating pulse rate and exercise.	Pairs. Investigation. Discussion.	79
Exercise keeps the body healthy.	2c (KS1)/Health: Looking after oneself, Level B	Discussion about benefits of exercise. Survey of amount of exercise one family do.	Whole class and individuals. Survey. Discussion. Using reference books.	81
Tobacco can be harmful.	2h/as above, Level B	Survey with questions for smokers and non-smokers. Discussion about dangers of smoking.	Whole class and individuals. Survey. Discussion.	83
Alcohol and drugs can be harmful.	2h/as above, Level C	Discussion about medicines, alcohol and drugs – uses and abuses. Preparing a talk about alcohol and drugs.	Whole class and small groups. Discussion. Preparing a 5-minute talk to present to the class.	84
Humans can reproduce.	2g/Living Things and the Processes of Life: Processes of Life, Level C	Discussion about the human life cycle. Sorting pictures into correct order. Writing about each stage.	Whole class and individuals. Discussion. Sorting. Writing about human life cycle.	85

Entries given in italics relate to the Scottish 5–14 Environmental Studies guidelines.

Living things & their Environment

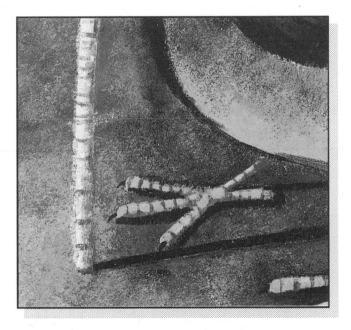

The activities in this section of the book encourage children to explore the characteristics and features of living things and their environments. In the course of carrying out the activities, children will gain experience in questioning, observing, predicting, recording, measuring and drawing conclusions. They will also have opportunities to work co-operatively and to share their ideas with others.

The activities will help to develop an understanding that living things have particular attributes in common and that there are life processes (such as nutrition, movement, growth and reproduction) which are common to all animals, including humans. The children will have the opportunity to use keys to identify plants and animals and will be encouraged to think about how plants and animals depend on each other in nature. The activities will help to develop an understanding of how animals are suited to their environments and how food chains show feeding relationships between living things.

LIFE PROCESSES
AND LIVING THINGS

LIVING OR NON-LIVING?

Things are living or non-living.

†† *Group or paired discussion, followed by whole-class discussion.*

🕐 *30–45 minutes.*

Previous skills/knowledge needed

Familiarity with the names and uses of ordinary things such as animals, plants, natural objects and manufactured objects.

Key background information

Living things are different from non-living things in several ways:

▲ They are able to grow through the chemical change of materials (some non-living things show growth – such as the expansion of a crystal – but they grow from the *same* material).

▲ They can excrete waste products (a car exhaust can get rid of waste, but it is not completely efficient).

▲ They are able to reproduce.

▲ They respond to stimuli (robots can be programmed to do this, but they can only respond to those stimuli chosen for them).

▲ They can respire.

▲ They contain a complex substance called ***protoplasm***.

▲ They need food to survive.

Resources needed

Photocopiable page 106, scissors, paper, pencils.

What to do

Hand out a copy of the photocopiable page to each child. Explain that you want them to decide which of the things on the sheet are living and which are non-living. Ask them to cut the sheet into picture cards and then sort the cards into the two groups. When they have all finished, ask them to share their results with another person or a small group. Do they agree? Ask them to discuss within the group (or pair) the differences and similarities between living and non-living things. One member of the group could record these differences and similarities.

The whole class can then discuss the results. Do the various groups agree? How do they disagree? Discuss items such as 'tree', 'wood' and 'book'. Draw up a whole class list of differences and similarities between living and non-living things. Look at things in the classroom – sort them into living and non-living. Does everyone agree? Make a large wall chart

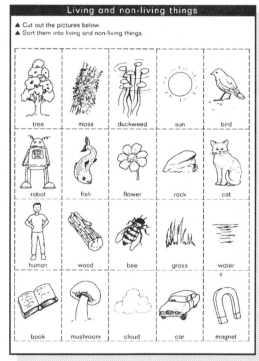

Living and non-living things

▲ Cut out the pictures below.
▲ Sort them into living and non-living things.

tree	moss	duckweed	sun	bird
robot	fish	flower	rock	cat
human	wood	bee	grass	water
book	mushroom	cloud	car	magnet

detailing the characteristics of living and non-living things. Cut out or draw pictures to add to each group.

Suggestion(s) for extension

Compare the similarities and differences between living things; for example, compare plants with animals. What do they both have in common? Find out about cells and tissues. What are they? Do non-living things have them?

Suggestion(s) for support

Provide a set of living things or pictures of living things for individual children to look at. What do these living things have in common with each other? Scribe the list of features for the child. Help the child to make decisions by asking questions such as: Can they all move? Do they all breathe? Can they all eat? Can they all produce young? Do the same with a set of non-living things. Then provide a mixed collection of things which are living and things which are non-living. Can the child sort these into the two groups? Ask the same questions, to help reinforce the list of characteristics.

Assessment opportunities

As the children are carrying out the activity, discuss with them their reasons for placing an object in either group. Can they tell you qualities that living things have and non-living things do not have? What information have they used to help them decide? Use two of the things on the sheet as an example – the fish and the rock, perhaps. Discuss the differences between them.

Opportunities for IT

As an extension to the main activity, children could be introduced to branching database software which they can use to develop a computer-based key in which information is sorted and classified. The software will also help to develop the ability to ask questions about living and non-living things which require a 'yes/no' answer, and is an excellent way to develop language skills. The activity is best done in small groups.

Display ideas

Take photographs of living and non-living things in and around the school (including the people!) Display these on the wall, using a different-coloured background for each group. Place a table in front of the wall. Make three signs saying: 'Living things', 'Non-living things' and 'Look at the photographs above. Sort these sentences into the correct group.' Then

write the following on cards, twice: 'Can have young', 'Can move', 'Is made up of many parts', 'Can eat', 'Needs to breathe', 'Made by humans', 'Found in nature', 'Able to grow', 'Found outdoors', 'Found indoors'. The children can then sort the sentences using two small hoops labelled 'living' and 'non-living'. Provide strips of card and a pencil, so the children can add characteristics of their own.

Other aspects of the Science PoS covered
Experimental and Investigative Science – 3b, c.

Reference to photocopiable sheet
Page 106 is used as a basis for the lesson, but could also be used later to assess retention of knowledge.

WHAT DO LIVING THINGS HAVE IN COMMON?

Many living things have common characteristics.
♰♰ *Paired or small-group observations, followed by whole-class discussion.*
🕐 *30 minutes for each observation. 20 minutes discussion.*

Previous skills/knowledge needed
Living things are different from non-living things. Plants and animals are living things.

Key background information
All living things have certain characteristics in common. They can all grow, excrete waste products, consume food, reproduce, respire, move and respond to stimuli.

Preparation
Provide a small selection of living things, such as potted plants, woodlice, mealworms, goldfish and small mammals (such as hamsters). Find out about the living conditions required for each one, to ensure that they do not come to any harm and that you have the necessary food and shelter. Check LEA guidelines on keeping live animals in school.

Resources needed
Paper, pencils, pictures of living things, actual living things (plants, small animals).

What to do
Divide the class into pairs or small groups and arrange for each group to have access to two different types of animals. This may mean that different groups have to work on different days. Provide the group with, say, some woodlice and some goldfish in suitable living conditions, and tell them to observe the two types of animal very closely.

Ask them to write down the things the two types of animal have in common. Ask questions to guide their observations, such as: Do they both move? How do they move? Can they move forwards, backwards, sideways? Can they turn round? Can you see them eating? What do they use to eat with? What do they eat? Can you see them breathing? Do they respond in some way if you put your hand near them? Do they prefer the dark or the light? Do the two types of animal have any body parts which are the same? Which body parts are different? Can you see any young? Are all the animals of the same type the same size, shape and colour?

Next, ask the group to compare a potted plant with an animal. What things can they observe which are the same on both? What features of plants do they know about that make plants similar to animals? (Growing or respiring, for example.)

Encourage the group to make an agreed list of things which they think all living things have in common. Discuss the results with the whole class. Points of disagreement should be noted and time allowed at a later date for the children to investigate these issues.

Provide pictures of living things and ask the children if all of these meet the agreed list of common characteristics.

Suggestion(s) for extension
Using pictures of and information about a wide selection of living things, make a list of the aspects which they have in common and the aspects which are different. Sort the living things into groups. This will lead on to a system of classification and will develop the notion that while living things have much in common, they also vary in many ways.

LIFE PROCESSES
AND LIVING THINGS

Suggestion(s) for support

Provide the children with a list of characteristics to be ticked off during observation. The list could include: it moves; it can move forwards; it can move backwards; it can move sideways; it can feed; it moves away when I put my hand near it; and so on. If a child has difficulty in reading the list independently, read the list with the child or pair off the child with a more capable reader.

Assessment opportunities

A concept map, as shown in Figure 1, is a very useful tool for assessment purposes. It enables the child to demonstrate her understanding of the relationships between particular things without having to write lengthy, detailed descriptions. A concept map consists of words and linking lines. Along the lines are written sentences or words which explain how the two aspects are connected with each other.

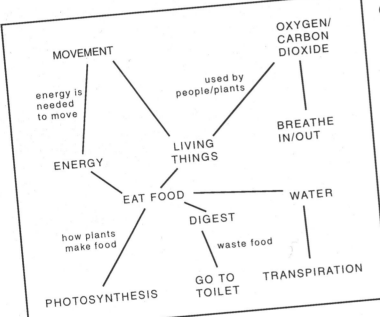

Figure 1: A concept map drawn by an eleven-year-old.

Concept maps could be used as a form of summative assessment at the end of a unit of work on living things, or they could be used at the end of this activity to assess what the child has understood about living things.

Display ideas

Ask the children to draw the living things which they have observed. Take photographs as well; then mount these pictures on the wall, together with a list of agreed characteristics which the living things all have in common. Place some picture cards of other living things on a table in front of the wall display. Make a sign challenging the children to sort the things into groups of their own choice. Ask them to give their reasons for grouping them as they have.

Other aspects of the Science PoS covered

Experimental and Investigative Science – 2b, c; 3b, c.

MOVEMENT IN ANIMALS

All animals move.

✝✝ *Individuals, pairs or small groups.*

🕐 *45 minutes observation. 30–60 minutes research. 20 minutes whole-class discussion.*

Previous skills/knowledge needed

Animals are living things. Note-taking skills for observation and use of reference materials.

Key background information

All animals can move in some way, but some are more mobile than others. Some animals are fixed in one place (sessile) – such as the sea anemone, which is fixed to a surface but has moving tentacles which can capture food. It can also retract to avoid detection. The ability to move freely can be essential to an animal's chances of survival. Movement allows the animal to search for food, select a suitable habitat in which to live, find a mate and escape from predators. Some animals can swim, some can walk and some can fly. Different body parts are adapted to allow for particular movements; but these body parts may move in different ways in different animals. Sometimes the same movement may be carried out by different body parts in different animals. Not all swimmers, for example, swim in the same way: jellyfish float; squids use jets of water; penguins use flippers; fish use their tails and fins. Movement in vertebrate animals is usually achieved through the action of the muscles and the skeleton.

Preparation

Obtain some minibeasts, such as snails, mealworms or woodlice, which are easy to keep. Ensure that they have the living conditions necessary to survive. Check LEA guidelines on keeping live animals in school.

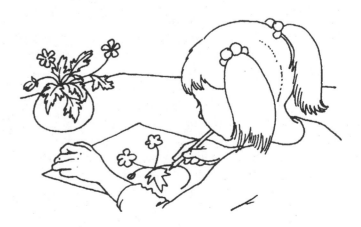

Resources needed

Paper, pencils, plastic Petri dishes or clear containers, plastic spoons, magnifying lenses, reference books on animals. (For investigation: resources needed will depend on the child's choice of question to investigate.)

What to do

Provide the children with some mealworms, woodlice or snails in a small, temporary home such as a plastic Petri dish or clear container. Tell them to observe the animals to see how they move. Provide hand-lenses for close observation.

Ask them questions to prompt their observations. Which body parts are used for movement? How many parts are used for movement? Do all these body parts move in the same way? Can the animal move backwards? Forwards? Sideways? Describe the movement – fast, slow, undulating, in waves? Ask the children to write down their observations. Ask them to draw the animal and label those body parts which can move.

Compare each group's observations. How different are the minibeast's movements from those of other animals or from our own movements? What advantages and disadvantages can the children suggest about the creature's methods of movement? Why is it necessary for the animal to move? Can the class agree on a list of reasons? Is it better for an animal to be fixed in one place or to be able to move freely? Why?

The children could then carry out their own investigations into the mechanisms of movement in woodlice, snails or mealworms. Questions to get them started might include: What could make a difference to how fast a woodlouse moves? Do bigger woodlice move faster than smaller ones? How well do woodlice/snails move on different kinds of surface?

Suggestion(s) for extension

As a follow-up to this lesson, the children could use reference books to find out how other animals move. Can they find out which animals can walk, swim or fly? Encourage them to look for common types of appendage used for movement – for example, are the legs of all walking animals similar in some way? How are they similar? How are a bird's feet adapted for walking and, in the case of water birds, for swimming? Do all animals that swim move in the same way? Do all flying animals have feathers? And so on.

Suggestion(s) for support

Start off the activity with a more familiar animal: humans. What body parts do we use for movement? What kinds of movement can be made with the head? Arms? Legs? Why is it necessary to move? Do we all move in a similar way? Sit with the children during the minibeast observation sessions and act as scribe if necessary when recording, or pair off the children so that one child can record for each pair.

Assessment opportunities

This activity will enable the teacher to assess how well the children can record their observations. The investigation will enable the teacher to assess aspects of Experimental and Investigative Science.

Opportunities for IT

If children are involved in extension activities to research information, they may be able to use one of the growing number of CD-ROM encyclopaedias. Pupils can develop the skills of searching for information and narrowing down information for a specific purpose. Some content-specific CD-ROMs, like *Creepy Crawlies* (Usborne), are available which fit this topic area specifically.

Display ideas

Draw, or cut out, pictures of body parts used for movement in a wide variety of animals. Label the body parts and write a label to explain how the part helps that animal to move. Mount these on the wall, together with the children's own observational drawings and notes from their investigation. Place a vivarium containing the minibeasts on a table in front of the wall display. Provide some hand-lenses and encourage the children's observations by writing questions on card for display near the vivarium. Questions might include: Which animals have similar legs to these? How many legs do insects have? Can you tell if these animals are able to fly? What other animals can fly? Why are these animals moving? Why do other animals need to move?

Other aspects of the Science PoS covered

Experimental and Investigative Science – 2b, 3b. (For the investigation: Experimental and Investigative Science – 1a, b, c, d, e; 2a, b, c; 3a, b, c, d, e.)

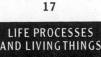
LIFE PROCESSES
AND LIVING THINGS

FEEDING IN ANIMALS

All animals feed.

✝✝ *Small group or whole class discussion. Paired research, data handling and observations.*

🕐 *Discussion – 20–30 minutes. Research and data collection – 30–60 minutes. Data handling (IT application) – 30 minutes. Observations – 5–10 minutes daily.*

Previous skills/knowledge needed

Familiarity with working from reference books. Familiarity with using a data handling computer program (see the IT links chart on page 159).

Key background information

All animals have to eat. Food, once consumed, is converted into simpler substances which can be used by the cells in the animal's body. Food provides the animal with energy and nutrients which enable it to live. The food of animals consists of other animals and/or plants.

Preparation

Obtain a selection of reference books about animals and what they eat. Select a suitable IT program for processing data. Purchase a selection of bird foods – nuts, seeds, and so on.

Resources needed

Reference books on animals (or photocopiable page 107 for learning support), pencils, an IT program for processing data, bird food, paper, pictures of animals.

What to do

Start off with a small-group or whole-class discussion about what animals eat. Begin with familiar animals such as cats, dogs, budgies, hamsters and so on. Then hold up some pictures of wild animals and ask the same question. Draw up a chart featuring the animals' names and what they eat. Ask the children why they think animals need to eat.

Explain to the children that they are going to find out about other animals and what they eat. Divide the class into pairs and ask the children to use reference books to find out the following things about their chosen animals: habitat, food, type of mouth, teeth, how many times they need to eat and their body size. This information can be collated on a survey sheet similar in format to Figure 1. You may need to qualify the answers in some way to assist the recording – for example, by agreeing on such things as how often the animal needs to eat. You may decide to use the categories: A – more than five times a day; B – less than five times a day; C – once every few days; D – once every few weeks. Information about teeth may just state whether the animal has them or not. Type of mouth may be defined as: A – beak; B – mouth; C – feeding tube; and so on.

After each pair have collected information on six different animals, they could enter the information into the IT program using the same headings as the survey sheet. The children could then use the program to find out the answers to questions such as: Which animals eat meat? Which animals eat plants? Which animals eat plants *and* meat? Which animals have teeth? Which animals need to feed more than five times a day?

Next, ask the children to discuss whether they have noticed any patterns or trends in the information. For example, is the size of the animal related to the number of times per day it needs to eat? Is the type of mouthparts related to the type of food eaten? Is there a correlation between the habitat in which an animal lives and the food it eats? You may have to enter quite a lot of data before some of these facts become apparent, so the data collection could continue over several weeks.

This work could be combined with an investigation into feeding habits. The children could find out which foods minibeasts prefer, using a vivarium to house them for a short period; or they could find out which foods birds prefer. One way to do this would be to set up several bird feeding stations around the school. Provide different foods at each station and ask the children to record which bird species visit each station. What conclusions can be drawn? Such a survey will provide the children with information about which foods they should leave out for the birds in their local area, and may help to establish an interest in setting up more permanent feeding stations at school or at home.

Suggestion(s) for extension

If they wish, children could go on to examine feeding in more detail. They could find out about the various types of beaks the birds have, for example, and how each type is adapted to the type of food eaten. They could look at the types of, and the purposes of, teeth in animals and could compare the teeth of carnivores to those of herbivores.

Figure 1

Animals and feeding

Name _____ Date _____

▲ Read each paragraph. Underline information about the animal's habitat, mouth type, teeth, food, body size and how often it eats. Use this information to complete your survey sheet.

Hedgehog
Hedgehogs are found in many countries in Europe. They sleep during the day and come out at night. Hedgehogs are between 20cm and 30cm long and weigh about 700g. They have a long snout which is used to dig for food. They eat caterpillars, beetles, worms, slugs, young mice and fruit. They tend to live in areas with bushes or shrubs, not in dense woods. The hedgehog hibernates during winter.

Emperor Penguin
This is the largest of all sea birds – length 112cm, weight 20–40kg. They live in the Antarctic. They live in large groups. They cannot fly, but are very good swimmers. They eat fish, squid and shrimps, and have a very sharp bill. They live on pack ice. The birds feed several times a day, but during the breeding season the male can go without food for up to 115 days. The male incubates the egg.

Green Turtle
This reptile is found in warm oceans and the Mediterranean Sea. It grows up to 1.5m in length and 185kg in weight. It can live to be 50 years old. It eats fish and crustaceans when young, but only eats plants when fully grown. It feeds many times a day. The turtle lays many eggs. They are buried on beaches in the sand. The Green Turtle has sharp, horny jaws, instead of teeth. It is a protected species.

Giant Panda
The Giant Panda is found in small areas of China. The male can grow to a height of 1.5m and can weigh up to 120kg. Pandas are very rare. They eat mainly bamboo, but also eat berries, fruit, flowers, fungi, grass, bark and sometimes birds' eggs. They need to eat many times each day (16 hours a day). They live in cold regions where bamboo grows. Giant pandas have large molar teeth. One of the main reasons why pandas are rare is that the areas where they live have been cleared for farming.

Suggestion(s) for support

The teacher could help those children who have difficulty using reference books by scribing the information for them or by providing these children with photocopiable page 107. This sheet carries information about animals which is relevant to the survey sheet and which is written in a more accessible format than would be found in most reference books. The teacher could also ensure that children who need support are paired off with children who are able to help them.

Opportunities for IT

Children could combine their information to make a class computer database about animal feeding. After class discussion, the teacher could create the database structure and pairs of children could enter their information into the database. Once the database has been set up, children could search for information and specific patterns or correlations (shape of beak and food eaten, or habitat and food).

Display ideas

Make models or draw pictures of foods eaten by animals. Display these on a wall, together with pictures of animals which eat these foods and labels showing their names. Place a table nearby, displaying some animals in their homes – such as goldfish, hamsters and so on – so that the children can observe them eating. Make question cards which encourage the children to look more closely at the animals' feeding habits: How often do they eat? Which foods do they eat first? Do they use other body parts to help them eat? Do they eat in groups or on their own? Do they store their food? Is the food eaten all at once? Display pictures of bird beaks and the foods those particular birds eat. Encourage the children to work out how the beak shape helps the bird to eat particular foods.

Other aspects of the Science PoS covered

Experimental and Investigative Science – 3b, c. (For investigation: Experimental and Investigative Science – 2a, b, c; 3a, b, c.)

Reference to photocopiable sheet

Page 107 has been designed to provide support for those children who find working from reference books difficult. It contains enough information for the children to complete the survey sheet on four animals.

BREATHING IN ANIMALS

All animals breathe.

†† *Whole-class discussion. Small-group observations.*

🕐 *30 minutes discussion. 10–20 minutes observation.*

Previous skills/knowledge needed

Animals are living things.

Key background information

All animals need to breathe. Animals absorb some of the oxygen from the air they breathe in and convert part of it into carbon dioxide in the air they breathe out. (They still breathe out more oxygen than carbon dioxide.) The oxygen absorbed is used by the animal's cells to release energy from food. Most animals have a transport system which carries oxygen and carbon dioxide to and from the cells.

Preparation

Make notes about the different types of breathing mechanisms used by animals (as mentioned in the 'What to do' section) to provide information for your talk to the class. Obtain some small animals (goldfish or small mammals), in suitable homes for observation. Check LEA guidelines on keeping live animals in school.

Animals and feeding survey sheet

Animal ———

Habitat ———

Mouth type ———

Teeth ———

Food ———

How often it eats ———

Size of animal ———

Figure 1

Resources needed

Pictures of mammals, birds, fish and insects; small animals for observation.

What to do

Tell the children that they are going to investigate how animals breathe. Ask them if they know how animals, such as mammals and fish, breathe. Can they tell you why animals need to breathe? What gases do the animals breathe in and out? Tell them that animals absorb some of the oxygen from the air they breathe in and convert part of it to carbon dioxide, which they breathe out. The oxygen is needed to help the cells in the body release energy from food.

Explain that different animals breathe in different ways. Tiny animals, such as flatworms, have bodies so small that no cell is far away from the outside of the body, so the various gases simply pass through the skin of the animal. Earthworms have a transport system in which capillaries run close to the surface of the skin, so that gases can be exchanged easily. (Explain that these capillaries are similar to those which turn our hands and faces red in hot weather.)

Larger animals have far more cells in their bodies, and therefore need more complex mechanisms for breathing. Explain that most land animals, like us, have *lungs* to breathe with. Ask the children to tell you how they think oxygen reaches the lungs. Explain briefly what happens in the lungs, and how capillaries in the lungs absorb oxygen which is then carried in the blood around the body. Show the children pictures of land-living vertebrate animals and of birds, and explain that these creatures all use lungs to breathe with.

Hold up some pictures of fish. Can the children say how fish breathe? Explain that most fish breathe through *gills*, which can be seen as slits in the side of the head. Inside are fine strands of tissue or *filaments,* beneath which are capillaries. Water is taken in through the mouth and is forced out over the gills. This allows gas exchange to take place.

Finally, show the children some pictures of insects and explain that the way in which they breathe is different from birds or fish. Insects have many small tubes called *tracheae*

which open up at the surface of the body. Air passes straight into these tubes.

Allow the children an opportunity to observe animals breathing at first hand. Let them observe goldfish to watch for the activity of the gills. Look at the mouth opening and closing. Can they see the gills moving? How often does the fish open and close its mouth? Make an observational drawing showing the location of the gills.

Also provide small mammals for observation. Count the number of times the animal breathes in one minute. Can the children compare this with their own breathing rate? Does the animal appear to breathe faster after exercise? Can they suggest why this might be?

Suggestion(s) for extension

Use reference books to find out what lungs, gills and tracheal systems look like. Draw the respiratory systems of a bird, a fish and an insect, labelling body parts. Purchase a fish from a fishmonger's or supermarket, and use it as the subject for closer examination and observational drawings of the gills.

Suggestion(s) for support

Divide the class (or those children who need support) into pairs. Ask each pair to tell each other what they can remember about the class discussion – then change pairs after two minutes, and again tell each other what they can remember. Change partners again after another two minutes. After the children have swapped information four or five times, bring them together again as a group and act as scribe while they tell you what they know about breathing in animals. Display their information as a group effort.

Display ideas

Make large headings – 'Breathes through skin', 'Breathes with lungs', 'Breathes with gills', 'Breathes with tracheae'. Ask the children to draw pictures of animals which belong in each group. Mount these on the wall, or use them to make mobiles.

Other aspects of the Science PoS covered

Experimental and Investigative Science – 2a, 3b.

LIFE PROCESSES
AND LIVING THINGS

ANIMAL LIFE CYCLES

All animals grow and reproduce.

†† *Whole-class or group discussion. Small-group research. Paired or small-group observations.*

🕑 *20–30 minutes whole-class discussion. 30–45 minutes research. 20–30 minutes observation.*

Previous skills/knowledge needed

Familiarity with sorting. How to use reference books to find information.

Key background information

All animals are capable of growth and reproduction. Animals need to reproduce in order to ensure that their species continues to survive. Simple animals, such as protozoa, reproduce themselves by dividing in two. Larger animals have developed different forms of reproduction: some (such as birds, amphibians and insects) lay eggs, and some (such as mammals and some fish) give birth to live young. The young do not always look like smaller versions of their parents. Most insects, for example, go through a life cycle which includes egg, larva, pupa and adult stages. The larva and pupa do not look like the adult, and these immature stages undergo a process of change or *metamorphosis*.

Preparation

Obtain reference materials which provide information about the life cycles of different animals. Obtain some animals, such as mealworms or frogspawn, and prepare suitable housing for them. Check LEA guidelines on keeping live animals in school.

Resources needed

Photocopiable pages 108 and 109 and/or page 110, pencils, scissors, pictures of animals, reference books on animals, live animals such as mealworms.

What to do

Tell the children that they are going to find out about how animals grow and change. Hand out a copy of photocopiable page 108 to each child. Provide them with scissors and ask them to cut up the sheet to make the animal cards. Explain that you are going to ask them a series of questions, each of which will require them to sort the cards into two groups.

Ask the children the questions given below. After each question, ask the children to sort the cards into two groups. They can then share their answers with a friend and, finally, with the class as a whole. Compare the results. This activity will help to elicit some of the things the children already know about animal reproduction.

Questions:

Which animals lay eggs?
Which animals feed their young?
Which animals have babies that look like their parents?
Which animals take a long time to grow into adults?
Among which animals do both parents look after the young?
Which animals build nests?
Which animals carry their young around with them?
Which animals spend part of their life in water and part on land?

You may think of other questions to ask. Ensure that the children sort quickly. They should not spend too long deciding, or the activity will become monotonous. Do not go into too

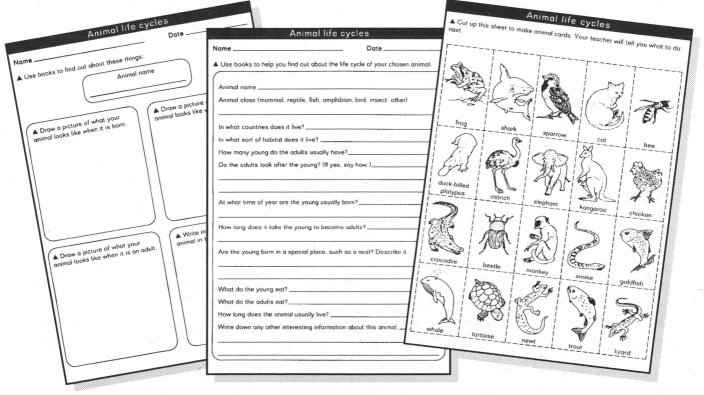

LIFE PROCESSES AND LIVING THINGS

much detail at this stage. Explain that they will find out more information in the next activity.

Next, divide the class into six groups to represent mammals, reptiles, amphibians, birds, fish and insects. Give each child in the group photocopiable page 109 and/or photocopiable page 110 and explain how to complete the sheet(s). Provide each group with reference books about their 'class' of animal, and ask them to find out about one animal from their 'class'.

When all groups have completed the task, bring the whole class together again to discuss the findings. Talk about the life cycles of the different animals, and how the young form may differ from the adult. Do some animals have more offspring than others? Can the children suggest why this might be? Which animals grow more quickly than others? Why might this be? Compare the life cycles of various animals to those of humans.

Provide an opportunity for the children to observe life cycles and growth in animals at first hand by setting up an aquarium containing mealworm beetles or tadpoles. Encourage the children to keep a daily diary of the changes which take place. Ask them to draw the different stages of development, and to list the similarities and differences between the stages. What advantages and disadvantages can they think of in a life cycle which involves a complete change of shape and function? What advantages are there in having large numbers of young? What are the advantages in having smaller numbers of young?

Suggestion(s) for extension

Compile a computer database on animal growth and reproduction using the information gathered. Possible headings could include: animal name, animal group, gestation period, usual number of offspring, adult height, adult weight, protects or abandons young, life cycle stages. Comparisons between animal groups could then be obtained and graphs produced to determine correlations (such as that between animal size and number of offspring).

Suggestion(s) for support

The teacher can act as scribe when the children are completing the worksheet, or a more able reader could be paired with a less able child to carry out the research. Children who need support could complete photocopiable page 110 rather than page 109, or the children could work in pairs with one child completing the written sheet (page 109) and the other child completing the drawings on page 110. Less able readers could form a small group working with the teacher who could read out the information to them so that they can complete the worksheet. This will allow discussion to take place as the research progresses.

Assessment opportunities

The sorting activity will enable the teacher to elicit information about what the children already know about animal growth and reproduction. The observation activity will provide opportunities to assess recording skills.

Opportunities for IT

Children could create group databases on specific types of animals, or combine their information to make a class database. They could then look for patterns relating to different types of animals, and display information graphically. Some databases will also allow children to include pictures of the animals.

Display ideas

Make mobiles showing the stages of growth in the life cycles of different animals. Take photographs of the mealworms and tadpoles as they grow, then mount and display the photographs alongside the children's observational drawings and notes. Make books about the stages of growth in

different animals with drawings, magazine pictures and photographs. Include information writing from the activity sheet.

Other aspects of the Science PoS covered
Experimental and Investigative Science – 2b; 3a, b, c.

Reference to photocopiable sheets
Photocopiable page 108 can be used by all the children for the sorting activity. More able children could complete both page 109 and page 110. Less able children could use photocopiable sheet 110 only.

SORTING LIVING THINGS

Living things can be sorted into groups.
†† *Small groups followed by whole-class discussion.*
🕐 *Group work 45–60 minutes. Class discussion 20 minutes.*

Previous knowledge/skills needed
There is a wide variety of living things. The ability to sort things into groups.

Key background information
All living things can be very broadly categorised as either animals or plants; but within each of these very large groups *(kingdoms)*, there are animals and plants with characteristics similar enough to form sub-groups of their own. Scientists do not agree on a single system of classification, but the following is one way of sorting animals into groups or *phyla*: protozoans (single-celled animals), poriferans (sponges), coelenterates (jellyfish), ctenophores (water-living animals with combs of filaments), flatworms, nematodes (roundworms), molluscs (animals with a body mantle, usually covered by a shell, and no limbs), annelids (segmented worms), arthropods (segmented bodies with a hard coating: crustaceans, spiders, insects), echinoderms (spiny-skinned invertebrates with radial body symmetry), chordates (animals with backbones: mammals, reptiles, fish, amphibians, birds, reptiles). Within each of these groups, there are further sub-groups. Plants are also divided into groups.

Preparation
Cut out 30 or 40 pictures of different animals from magazines. Stick each picture on to a separate piece of card. Collect a wide assortment of house plants. Collect together an assortment of everyday objects of different sizes, shapes, colours, textures and materials.

Resources needed
Animal pictures on card, house plants, a collection of everyday objects, paper, pencils.

What to do
Ask one child in the group to sort the collection of everyday objects in some way. Can the others in the group work out the criterion used for sorting? Challenge someone else in the group to sort them in a different way. Can each member of the group think of a different way of sorting? Write down the different criteria. How many ways can the group find? (Possible groupings may include: colour, shape, size, texture, what it is used for, what it is made of, with or without holes, and so on.)

Next, provide the group with a collection of house plants. Challenge them to sort the plants into groups in the same way that they did with the everyday objects. Ask them to record the criteria used. (Possible groupings may include: colour, shape, size, texture, type of leaves, with or without flowers, number of leaves, type of stem, and so on.)

Finally, provide the group with the pictures of animals on cards and ask them to sort these also. In how many different ways can they be sorted? (Possible groupings may include: colour, size, body covering, how they move, where they live, what they eat, number of legs, with or without wings, and so on.)

When all groups of children have had a turn at sorting, bring the whole class together to compare the results. How many different ways could be found for sorting each collection? Make a list of the criteria used. Can some criteria be used for all collections? Which criteria are suitable for sorting animals but not plants? Discuss how the results of sorting may vary depending on the objective of the sorting process. Can the children suggest why scientists may want to sort living things into groups?

Suggestion(s) for extension

This activity could be extended by researching the various animal and plant groups that scientists have classified. Can the children find out the characteristics of mammals, reptiles, amphibians, birds, and so on.

They could enter information about several animals or plants from each group into a computer data-handling program, in order to build up a computer file on each group, and then access information about them in further studies.

Suggestion(s) for support

With each collection, the teacher could start off by sorting the things for the children. She might begin by saying that she is going to sort by colour, and asking the children to help her. Then she could sort the collection in a different way and ask the children to guess the criterion used. Once the children understand how the sorting can be carried out, they could try it themselves – first working in pairs, then working individually if appropriate.

Display ideas

Ask the children each to draw one way in which they could sort the collections of living things. Mount these on the wall above a table on which the actual collections are displayed. Put up a sign to challenge the children to think up other ways of sorting, and add their drawings of these to the display. Mount some pictures of animals or plants, which are grouped in some way, on the wall. Put up a list of the criteria for sorting used for each group. Then place some small hoops and pictures of other living things on a table, and put up a sign asking the children to sort these pictures into the groups according to the criteria listed on the wall.

Other aspects of the Science PoS covered

Experimental and Investigative Science – 2b, 3b.

▣ INTRODUCING KEYS

Keys can be used to classify living things.
♙ *Small groups or whole class, sometimes working in pairs.*
🕐 *30–45 minutes.*

Previous skills/knowledge needed

Living things can be sorted into groups. Living things have common characteristics. Basic features of mammals, reptiles, amphibians, birds and fish.

Key background information

Keys are often used in science to identify the name of a living thing or the group to which it belongs. Keys can take different forms, but most involve working through a set of questions or descriptions until you find the name or group which best fits the thing you are trying to classify. Keys also help us to look more closely at the characteristics of a living thing.

Preparation

Draw the following chart on a large piece of paper or on a chalkboard:

1	Has feathers	*bird*
	Has no feathers	**go to 2**
2	Has hair or fur	*mammal*
	Has no hair or fur	**go to 3**
3	Has fins	*fish*
	Has no fins	**go to 4**
4	Has scales	*reptile*
	Has no scales	*amphibian*

Resources needed

Photocopiable pages 111 and 112, scissors, adhesive, pencils, paper, the chart above; pictures of a bird, a mammal, a fish, a reptile and an amphibian.

What to do

Show the children the chart you have prepared and explain that this is an example of what is known as a key, and that keys can be used to find out the names of living things. Explain that to use this key, you start at number 1 and choose the correct statement, then move on to number 2 and so on. Demonstrate how this works by holding up a picture of a fish and going through each stage of the key until you reach number 3, where the picture fits. Repeat this with some of the other pictures, so the children understand the process.

Next, hand out copies of photocopiable page 111 and tell the children that this is an example of another type of key. Can they tell you how it differs from the first key? Explain

LIFE PROCESSES AND LIVING THINGS

that with this key, you need to answer the question with a yes or a no and follow the path to find out what the animal is. First ask them to look at picture D on the sheet. Go through the questions with the children until you come to the right answer. Ask them to fill in the word 'spider' next to the letter D at the bottom of the page. Then ask them to work in pairs, or individually, to use the rest of the key.

Now hand out copies of photocopiable page 112 and explain that this is a similar type of key to the one just used, but it involves more animals. Ask the children to work in pairs, or individually, to complete it. To do this, they need to cut out the animals at the bottom of the page and stick them in the correct places on the key. When they have all finished, ask the children to share their results. Do they all agree? Can they tell you when it would be most useful to use a key? In what ways do keys help us?

Challenge the children to make up a key like the one you first showed them on the board or chart, using the animals from photocopiable page 112.

Suggestion(s) for extension

Ask the children to make up a key as on photocopiable page 112, using the same animal pictures that were used with the first key they looked at.

Suggestion(s) for support

Pair up children who are less able readers with better readers, so they can work together when using photocopiable page 112. Encourage the children to look closely at the pictures of the animals to see whether they have legs/wings and so on. Act as scribe when the children are making their own key, or pair up a more able child with a less able one.

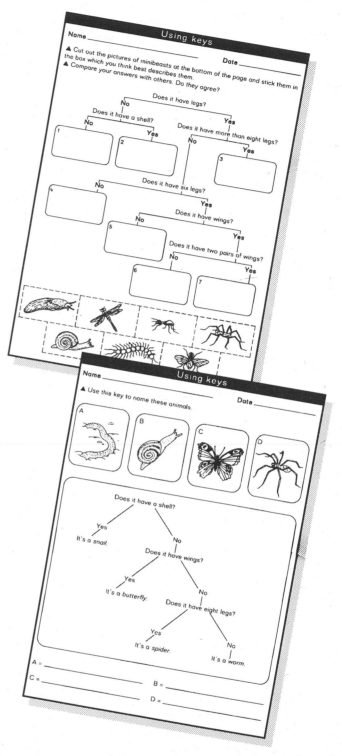

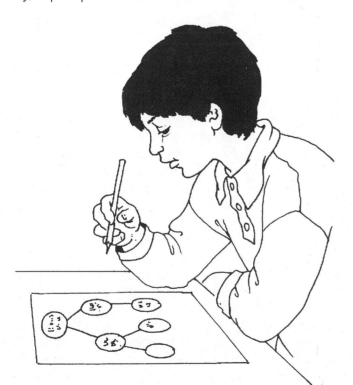

Opportunities for IT

This activity can be extended to include the use of a computer branching database. Children must 'teach' the database differences between items by asking questions which have a 'yes/no' answer. The computer then creates a key which can be used by another child to identify any item included within the key. The creation of the key is an excellent language development activity.

This is best done with children working in small groups. Before they start to use the computer, give the children an opportunity to use a completed branching database so that they can get a feel for the way it works and the type of questions asked. Make sure that the group has access to the full range of items to be included within the key, and that they spend some time looking at them and sorting them into sets using different criteria. Probably the most important decision to be made is which initial question to ask. Ideally, it should split the full set into two fairly equal parts. Once this has been done, they can start to enter their information into the branching database, following the instructions which appear for each new question. When the database is completed, the children should check it among themselves

to make sure that it works, then try it out with other children. Some versions of the software allow the children to print out the completed database in key format, which is ideal for displays or for checking where questions do not work.

Display ideas
Make up other simple keys as shown on the photocopiable pages. Draw them out on card, then cover them with clear, adhesive plastic and set them out on a table for the children to use. The keys can be written on with felt pen, then wiped clean and used again. Mount the children's own keys that they have made on card, and stick them up on the the wall near the table. Make 'key' mobiles.

Other aspects of the Science PoS covered
Experimental and Investigative Science – 2b, 3b.

Reference to photocopiable sheets
Answers to photocopiable page 112: *1* – slug, *2* – snail, *3* – centipede. *4* – spider, *5* – ant, *6* – housefly, *7* – dragonfly.

USING KEYS IN THE LOCAL ENVIRONMENT

Keys can help to identify living things in the local environment.
†† *Whole class working in pairs or small groups.*
🕐 *45–60 minutes.*

Previous skills/knowledge needed
There is a wide variety of living things in the environment. Living things can be sorted into groups. How to use an identification key.

Key background information
Simple identification keys can be very useful for identifying living things in the environment. They can often be more practical than reference books, because they encourage the children to look closely at the various parts of a living thing and to compare one living thing with another.

Preparation
Decide on a suitable site in or near the school grounds to take the children on a walk. It is important that the site should contain a wide enough variety of living things for children to use the keys successfully. Obtain permission, if necessary, to visit the site and take note of any possible safety considerations, for instance when visiting a pond or stream. Arrange for extra adult help if necessary.

Resources needed
Photocopiable pages 113, 114, 115 and 116, hand-lenses, magnispectors, rulers, plastic bags, clipboards, pencils, paper, a camera (optional).

What to do
Discuss the outing with the children before leaving school. Work out a suitable 'country code' with them – not to leave litter, to return things to where they were found, to return animals to their environment as soon as possible, not to take large plant samples, and so on. Discuss safety issues, which may include not touching fungi (as some are poisonous), keeping together in a group, taking care at the water's edge, and so on.

Allow the children the opportunity to use the hand-lenses and magnispectors before the walk, so that they know how to use them correctly. Explain that plant samples can be collected only from what is found loose on the ground, not from living plants. Make sure that each child knows how to use the identification keys.

During the walk, ask the children to select five different animals and five different plants and then use the keys to try to identify them. They could draw each thing they select and make observational notes. Comments about a plant could

include: size, shape, where it is growing, colours, leaf shapes and whether it has fruits, seeds or flowers. Comments about an animal could include: where it was found, number of legs, number of wings, how it moves, size, shape and colours. A camera could be used to keep a record of things found and where they were found. Appoint some children to collect leaf samples and others to collect bark or seeds.

After sufficient time has passed, gather the children together to compare the plants and animals which have been found. Were all the different types of plants on the key found? Were all the different types of animals found? How easy did the children find it to use the keys? Do they want to find out more information about some of the things they have found? Where could they look to find this out? Make a list of all the things found.

Back at school, discuss the leaf, bark and seed collections with the children to help them make their own keys for sorting these collections. Use reference books to identify those things that could not be classified using the keys.

Suggestion(s) for extension
Use more advanced and more detailed keys for identifying different types of invertebrates or plants.

Suggestions(s) for support
Some children could just concentrate on one group, either of plants or of animals. Less able readers could be partnered with children who are good readers to help in reading the keys, or photocopiable page 111 could be used instead. The teacher can help to record observational notes by acting as scribe, or portable tape recorders could be used.

Opportunities for IT
Children could create their own key using a computer branching database. They have to 'teach' the database the differences between items by asking questions which have a 'yes/no' answer. The computer then creates a key which can be used by other groups to identify any item within the key. The creation of the key is an excellent language development activity.

Children could also use a simple word processor or drawing package to create a printed version of their key. Simple drawing packages enable children to arrange words anywhere on the screen and then draw the linking lines to create a key. More able pupils could also add pictures taken from clip art resources, or ones they have drawn themselves and scanned into the computer.

Display ideas
Mount larger versions of the plant and animal keys on the wall. Add the children's observational drawings of things found on the walk in the correct places on the keys. Display the children's notes and other drawings, plus any photographs taken. Put the collection of seeds, leaves and bark on a table, together with an identification key designed by the children.

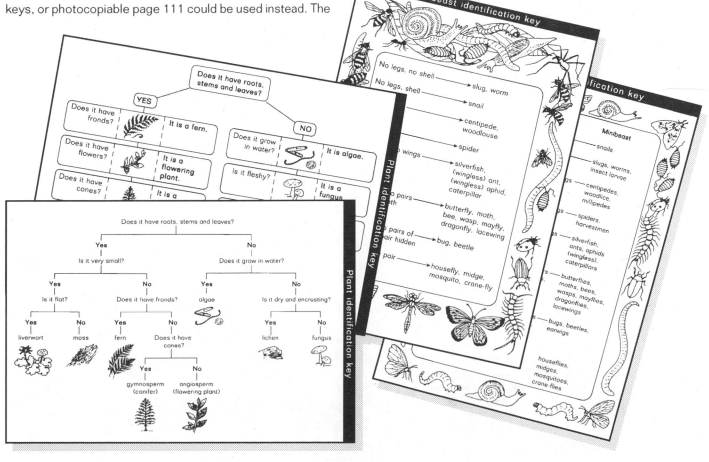

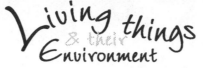
Put up a sign asking people to sort the collection according to the key.

Other aspects of the Science PoS covered
Experimental and Investigative Science – 2b, 3b.

Reference to photocopiable sheets
The sheets show four different examples of keys. None will provide a detailed identification of living things, but they will all provide the children with an opportunity to use keys in the environment. Select the key(s) which you think are appropriate to the children who will be using them.

HABITATS

Different plants and animals are found in different habitats.
†† *Small groups.*
⏱ *60–120 minutes.*

Previous knowledge/skills needed
How to use keys or reference materials to identify plants and animals.

Key background information
A habitat is the place where living things live. It is more than just a home, and includes the whole surrounding area from which living things are able to obtain all that they need to live. Most plants and animals are specially adapted to survive in a particular habitat, and have developed special features to suit the demands of their environment. Thus different habitats support different plants and animals.

Preparation
Select four different sites near your school which demonstrate four different habitats – for example, a pond, a grassy area, woodland and a dry, stony area. Obtain permission, if necessary, to visit these sites and make a note of any safety aspects which may need consideration. Ensure that the children know about the visit well in advance, so that suitable clothing and parental permission can be organised. Make sure you have enough adult supervision for your outing, especially if visiting a pond or other water site. If appropriate, allow the children time to learn how to use lenses, magnispectors and so on before leaving school, to make sure that they know how to use them during field studies.

Resources needed
Small plastic hoops, hand-lenses, magnispectors, reference books or identification keys, plastic spoons, white plastic trays or ice-cream containers, plastic bags, coloured pencils, paper, clipboards, pencils, a camera.

What to do
Explain to the children that they are going to visit four different sites to look at the animals and plants living there. Discuss with them how they should behave when they visit the sites, and agree on a 'country code of conduct' – leave things as you find them, return animals to where they were found, leave no litter, close gates, keep to paths, and so on.

Before visiting the sites, ask the children to tell you what kinds of plants and animals they think they will find in each area. Keep a record of their predictions to compare with their actual observations on the day. Ask the children to give reasons why they think these particular things will be found in that particular area. What do they base their predictions on?

Give each group of children a small plastic hoop, hand-lenses, plastic bags and a pen and paper to record what they find. At each site, choose a spot to place the hoop on the ground and ask the children to concentrate solely on the area inside the hoop. Ask them to record the things they

find there in some way. They may write about, and draw, what they see; and one leaf from each type of plant could be collected and taken back to school as a permanent record. Take photographs of each site.

Encourage the children to use books or keys to help them identify what they find. Questions to prompt them to look more closely might include: Which type of plant is most common in this area? Which type of animal is most common? Are the leaves of the plants similar or very different? Are the colours of the animals a good camouflage, or do the animals stand out clearly? What is the soil like in this area? Is there a lot of dead matter? Are the animals hiding? Where? Can you count the number of animals in your hoop area?

If a closer examination of an animal is needed, use the plastic spoons to transfer it to a container. Remember to keep water creatures in a small amount of the water from which they were taken, and to keep the container in the shade. Some pond creatures are carnivores, so try to keep these separate from other animals. Always return the animals to their habitat as quickly as possible.

Once back at school, discuss the things that were found in each area. Can patterns be discovered? Do different types of animals and plants live in the different sites? (Was enough evidence collected to provide an answer to this?) Are some plants or animals found in more than one area, or in all areas? Are water plants different from land plants? In what ways? Do the colours of the living things vary from site to site? Would this help to protect them (camouflage)? Are the water plants anchored in a different way from land plants? Why might this be? Consider the children's earlier predictions. Did their findings match their predictions? Were the children surprised at what they found? Why/why not? Why do they think particular insects, for example, live where they do? What things do these animals need to live? Can the children say what particular plants need to survive?

Suggestion(s) for extension
Investigate which animals of a particular type live in different habitats. For example, find out which mammals live in deserts, rainforests, fresh water, sea water, grassy plains and woodland. Describe the habitat in each case. What features do the animals which live in each habitat share? What features are different?

Suggestion(s) for support
Take photographs of the animals and plants found on the nature walk, rather than drawing and writing about them at each site. Use portable tape-recorders to give a description of the site and what was found there, to provide a more permanent record and to aid in recollection. Use the samples of leaves to look more closely at the differences between the plants at each site. Ask questions to help the children consider the differences, such as: Are the colours/shapes/textures/sizes different? Which site had the widest variety of living things? Which had the least variety? Can the children say why this was the case?

Opportunities for IT
Children might use a CD-ROM to find information about the living specimens found in each habitat. Some of this information might be recorded using a word processor.

Children could also work in groups to put together a multimedia presentation on a particular habitat. This might include children's writing, pictures taken from CD-ROMs, scanned drawings or maps made by the children, digitised photographs taken with the school video camera and sounds recorded from a tape recorder. These can be combined in a multimedia authoring package.

Display ideas
Make large murals of each site with drawings and paintings of the plants and animals found there. Include three-dimensional models. Add the children's writing, photographs, observational drawings and notes about each area. Name the animals and plants which can be identified. Press the samples of plants and attach them to card using clear self-adhesive plastic. Add these to the display. Make mobiles of the flying animals observed in each area.

Other aspects of the Science PoS covered
Experimental and Investigative Science – 1a, e; 2a, b; 3a, b, c, d, e.

PLANTS AND THEIR ENVIRONMENT

Plants are suited to their environment.

†† *Whole class divided into pairs.*

🕐 *60–120 minutes.*

Previous skills/knowledge needed

Plants are living things. There is a wide variety of types of plant, and different plants are found in different habitats.

Key background information

Plants living on land have different characteristics from water plants. Water acts as a support for aquatic plants. This means that their stems and roots are sometimes less well-developed than in land plants. Land plants need to obtain water from the soil, so their root systems are sometimes very large. Leaves in land plants are often more rigid than in aquatic plants, since they have to support themselves. Light is absorbed by water, so most aquatic plants need to grow near the surface. Land plants are adapted to minimise water loss and avoid the effects of high temperatures.

Preparation

Select a suitable location where a comparison can be made between land and water plants, such as a pond and a meadow or a stream and a wood. Obtain permission to visit the site if necessary. Make a checklist of any safety precautions you think may be needed. Arrange for other adults to act as helpers, since close supervision is usually necessary when visiting water sites. Ensure that the children have the necessary clothing for such an outing.

Resources needed

Photocopiable page 117, clipboards, pencils, paper, hand-lenses, reference books or identification keys, measuring tapes.

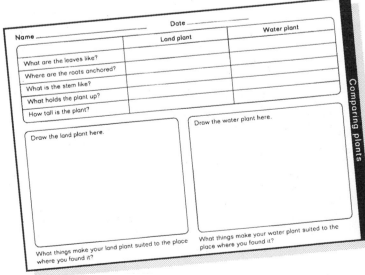

What to do

Explain to the children that they are going to visit two different places to look at the plants which grow there. At each site they are going to choose one plant to study closely. Explain how to complete photocopiable page 117. Discuss how to behave when at the site itself, and develop a class code of behaviour: do not throw things into the water, don't take specimens away, replace everything as you find it, try not to tread on the plants near the water's edge, and so on.

At each site, allow the children time just to sit and look before observing in more detail. What can they say in general about the plants they can see? Are they of different heights? Colours? Of many different kinds or one main type? Are certain types grouped together? Are there plants in shady/sunny areas? The children could draw a rough outline map of the area, showing where the plants are situated.

Then ask the children to have a closer look at the plants found in each site. Ask them to choose one plant from each site, and to use the photocopiable page to note down information in more detail. Encourage them to use the hand lenses to look closely at the surfaces of leaves and stems. At each site ask questions to guide the children's observations: How is the plant anchored? What are the leaves like? What is the surface of the leaf like? Are the leaves hard or soft? How are the leaves arranged on the stem? What size is the plant? Is the stem hard or soft? Where do you think the plant

LIFE PROCESSES AND LIVING THINGS

gets its water and nutrients from? Can sunlight reach all the leaves? Is the plant alone or in a group?

Once the children have made their observations at each site, gather them together again as one group, either outside or back at school. Ask them to consider the differences and similarities between a land plant and a water plant. Is the need for support different? What provides the support for many water plants? What things do land plants have that make them strong and give them support? How do water plants get enough sunlight? Where do water plants get their nutrients from? Where do land plants get water from? What parts of land plants are used to take in this water? Are the roots of land plants and water plants different? How? Why? What problems might land plants encounter that water plants would not have? How could land and water plants disperse their seeds? How do water plants, such as the lily, make sure that their flowers can be pollinated?

After this discussion ask the children to write down the features of land and water plants that help them to make the best use of the environment in which they live.

Suggestion(s) for extension
Find out how plants from other habitats have adapted to their environment – those from deserts, rainforests, Arctic areas, grasslands, and so on.

Suggestion(s) for support
Obtain a water plant, such as Canadian pondweed, and a potted house plant, such as a goosefoot plant. Look at the similarities and differences between their leaves, stems and roots. Compare the strength or rigidity of the plants. Can the child suggest why there is a difference? Help the children to complete their photocopiable sheets during the walk.

Opportunities for IT
Children could also use a CD-ROM encyclopaedia to search for information on how plants have adapted to other environments. If children create a habitats display, they could word-process labels or notes to accompany the display using a word processor or DTP package.

Display ideas
Make a large mural of a water site and a land site. Add drawings of plants which are found in each area. Attach labels showing the features of the plants which make them suited to their environment. Make a book about land and water plants, using the children's drawings and notes.

Other aspects of the Science PoS covered
Experimental and Investigative Science – 2b, 3b.

Reference to photocopiable sheet
Help those children who are experiencing difficulties to read the sheet, or pair up good readers with less able readers.

ANIMALS AND THEIR ENVIRONMENT

Animals are suited to their environment.

†† *Pairs.*

🕐 *30–45 minutes. Research over several sessions.*

Previous skills/knowledge needed
Animals are living things. There is a wide variety of animals. Different animals are found in different habitats.

Key background information
Animals living in different environments are adapted in different ways to those environments. All birds, for example, have similar characteristics; but many water birds have features (such as webbed feet) which are different from those of birds that spend their time on land. Some animals are *camouflaged* to blend in with their surroundings. Aquatic animals are *streamlined* to move more easily in water. Some animals *hibernate* to avoid extremes of cold when food is scarce. Digging animals have strong, sharp front feet. And so on.

Resources needed
Photocopiable page 118 (or page 119 for support), scissors, paper, pencils, reference books on animals.

What to do
Provide each child with a copy of photocopiable page 118 and ask them to try to match up each sentence with the animal which possesses that feature. (Some sentences may

LIFE PROCESSES AND LIVING THINGS

Animals and their environment (1)

▲ Cut out the animals and sentences below.
▲ Match up each sentence to the animal you think has that special feature.
Some animals may match with more than one sentence.

Pond animals
frog
diving beetle

Woodland animals
badger
squirrel
woodpecker
umber moth
mallard
stickleback

Has a long snout for sniffing and digging up food.	Has waterproof feathers.
The young are born in a protective jelly which floats.	Has webbed feet to help it swim.
Has special hairs on its hind legs to help it swim.	Has young which feed on oak leaves.
Has a filter in its bill to sift food from mud.	Has fins for swimming.
Its body is camouflaged to protect it from enemies.	Has a strong skull for hammering at wood.
Has a thin, damp skin to help it breathe on land and in water.	Can hibernate in winter when food is scarce.
Has very strong claws for digging.	Has specially-adapted legs for climbing trees.

Animals and their environment (2)

Land animal – badger
long snout for sniffing food
grey coat to help it hide in bushes
sharp claws for digging
strong legs for running
keeps young in a burrow (set)

webbed feet for swimming
long tongue for catching insects
lays eggs in water
strong le[gs] for jump[ing]

A frog is well suited to living in water. It has webbed feet to help it swim. It has good _____ so it can see its enemies. It has a long tongue for catching _____. The frog's skin is thin and damp to help it _____. It lays _____ in water and young tadpoles grow from the eggs. The frog has strong legs which help it to _____ and webbed feet which help it to _____.

A badger is well suited to living on land. It has sharp _____ for digging. It keeps its young in a _____ called a set. It has strong legs to help it _____. The badger has good _____ so it knows when an enemy is approaching. It uses its long _____ to sniff out food on the ground. Its grey _____ helps it to hide in the bushes.

What differences are there between the features of desert animals and Arctic animals? Why are some animals camouflaged and not others? Consider the differences between species of one animal type – birds, for example. Look at the differences in beaks and feet, and how these are adapted to different circumstances.

Suggestion(s) for extension
Visit a pond and compare the invertebrates found there with those found in a wood or garden. What similarities and differences are there? What features do aquatic animals have that land animals do not need? How different are land beetles from water beetles? How do the animals breathe, feed and move in each environment?

Suggestion(s) for support
Work with the children as they are carrying out the investigation with the activity sheet (page 118), or use photocopiable page 119 instead. Help them to find out information using reference books. Make sure there are books at a suitable reading level for this research, or make up an information sheet of your own for one or two animals.

Opportunities for IT
Children might use a CD-ROM encyclopaedia to research information on animals and their environment and how animals are adapted to survive.

Groups, or pairs of children, could word-process their information to create a class book. If a DTP package is used the teacher could set up a 'master page' to provide a consistent format for the children to write to.

relate to more than one animal, and one animal may be described by more than one sentence.) Provide some reference books for children to use if they wish. Then ask them to work in pairs to compare and discuss their answers. Do they agree?

Discuss the results with the whole class. What other features does each of these creatures have which enable it to live in its environment? For example: How does a badger protect itself from enemies? Why does a frog have so many young? Why are the spawn wrapped in 'jelly'? How does the shape of a fish help it to move in water?

Working in pairs, the children can then use the reference books to find out about one animal and the special features which enable it to survive well in the habitat in which it lives. They could draw the animal and label the body parts which are especially adapted to its habitat.

After each pair have completed their research, discuss the findings with the whole class. What special features do water animals have which help them to live in water? How do land animals differ from water animals in their appearance?

Display ideas

Paint pictures of different environments such as a pond, a wood, a desert. Add pictures of animals found in these areas and labels pointing out the features which enable the animals to survive there. Make a book of the children's research.

Other aspects of the Science PoS covered

Experimental and Investigative Science – 2b, 3b.

Reference to photocopiable sheets

Page 118 – one animal may have more than one sentence which relates to it and one sentence may relate to more than one animal, so you may need to discuss how best to present the sorted sets. Two options are shown in Figure 1.

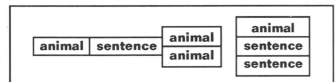

Figure 1

Page 119 – this can be used as a support sheet. All the necessary information about each animal is given. The child is required to fill in the correct words in the spaces.

HOW ANIMALS AND PLANTS HELP EACH OTHER

Plants and animals depend on each other.

†† *Whole-class discussion followed by paired or individual activity.*

⏰ *20–30 minutes discussion. 20–30 minutes activity.*

Previous skills/knowledge needed

Plants and animals live together in the environment.

Key background information

Plants and animals depend on each other for a wide variety of things. These include:

▲ **Food** – many animals eat plants, and in turn are eaten by other animals. Plants help to decompose dead animals, and some (including fungi) live as parasites of animals. Some plants kill and 'eat' insects. Some animals (including aphids) are parasites of plants.

▲ **Reproduction** – animals can aid the dispersal of plant seeds. Animals can also pollinate plants. Animals can use plants to build nests with, to lay eggs in, for help in mating rituals, and as shelter for their young.

▲ **Shelter** – many animals use trees and other plants as a home.

▲ **Protection** – many animals have a similar appearance to plants in order to camouflage themselves.

▲ **Gas exchange** – animals produce carbon dioxide (in breathing) which plants use; plants produce oxygen (by photosynthesis) which animals use.

Resources needed

Photocopiable page 120, pencils, pictures of animals and plants showing how they depend on each other (for example, bees visiting flowers, birds using nests, cows eating grass, insects that look like leaves, squirrels burying nuts, and so on).

What to do

Show the pictures to the children and ask them to tell you how plants and animals are helping each other in each example. Decide, if possible, which benefits more from the relationship. Use the chalkboard or a large piece of paper to write down the ways in which plants and animals help each other.

Divide the class into pairs and allow them a few minutes to discuss other ways that animals and plants depend on each other. Bring the whole class together again and share the results. If the children do not mention all of the

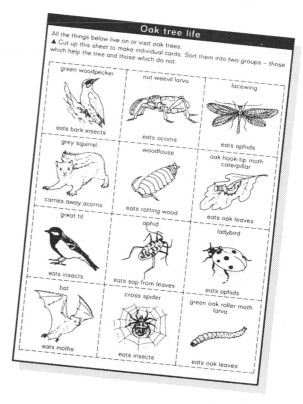

relationships listed in the background information section, tell them the ones they have missed. Use pictures to illustrate these points if possible.

Discuss some aspects in more detail. For example, seed dispersal – how some birds eat the seeds and then excrete them somewhere else, how furry animals can carry seeds in their coats, how some animals (such as squirrels) bury the seeds, and so on.

LIFE PROCESSES
AND LIVING THINGS

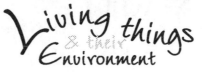

Hand out copies of photocopiable page 120 and explain that an oak tree provides examples of how plants and animals depend on each other. Ask the children to work in pairs, or individually, to complete the activity. They should cut out the pictures and decide whether the animal helps the oak tree in some way or causes it harm.

When everyone has finished, discuss the results with the whole class. Is everyone in agreement? Which do they think benefits the most: the tree or the things that depend on it? Can the children think of other plants and animals that might depend on an oak tree? If possible, visit a real oak tree and try to find evidence of the animals and plants living there.

Suggestion(s) for extension
Find out more about decomposers, parasites and pollinators, and how animals and plants benefit from each other.

Suggestion(s) for support
Pair up children who are good readers with less able readers when using the photocopiable sheet.

Opportunities for IT
Children could make short word-processed notes or labels to accompany the display about animals that live in an oak tree.

Display ideas
Paint a large oak tree and mount it on the wall. Draw animals and plants which use an oak tree in some way. Add these to the drawing of the tree, and use labels to explain how the plant and animal help each other. Ask the children to write down/draw ways in which animals and plants help each other, and use these to make a book or wall display.

Reference to photocopiable sheet
Animals which help the oak tree: woodpecker, lacewing, grey squirrel (by burying acorns which may grow into new trees), great tit, ladybird, bat, cross spider.

FOOD CHAINS (1)

Food chains show feeding relationships between living things.

†† *Whole-class discussion. Individuals or pairs for activity.*

⏱ *30–45 minutes.*

Previous skills/knowledge needed
Plants and animals are living things, and they depend on each other. How to use reference books.

Key background information
All living things in a particular area are connected with each other in some way and, together, form a community or *ecosystem*. Some living things are *producers* (green plants), some are *consumers* and some are *decomposers*. All are necessary for the whole ecosystem to survive. *Food chains* show the feeding relationships between the organisms in an ecosystem – a plant is eaten by an animal, which in turn is eaten by another animal, and so on until the carnivore at the top of the food chain is reached.

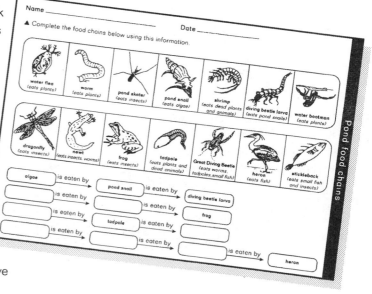

Preparation

Obtain reference books on ponds which provide information about the food that pond creatures eat.

Resources needed

Photocopiable page 121, paper, pencils, reference books on ponds, pictures of pond creatures, card, cotton, a hole punch, felt-tipped pens.

What to do

Provide each child with a copy of photocopiable page 121. Ask them to look closely at the diagram to see the kinds of animals that live in a pond. Have they seen any of these creatures in a real pond? Show the children larger pictures of the pond animals to highlight shapes, colours, sizes, names of body parts, and so on.

Explain that all of these living things need to find all the food they require in the pond itself. Discuss how plants can help to provide oxygen for animals to breathe, and how many animals use plants for food. Do the children know what the plants need to survive? Explain how one animal is eaten by another, which in turn may be eaten by another animal, and how this can be shown as a food chain. Apply this to animals they are more familiar with: for example, a rabbit eats grass and the rabbit is eaten by a fox or perhaps a human.

Explain how the photocopiable page shows food chains in a pond. Look at the first example and then ask the children to complete the others on their own or in pairs. Discuss their answers. Can they name other food chains involving the animals on the sheet? Talk about what might happen to the animals if all the plants died. Would any survive? If there were no larger animals to eat the insects, what might happen? Why do some animals leave the pond but return at certain times? Why do they need the pond?

Ask the children to use the reference books to find out what the animals eat, then write out other food chains which could be found in a pond. Discuss their findings. Which things in the pond are food for lots of other animals? Which things are only eaten by one or two animals? Which is the longest food chain they can find? What might happen if the pond became polluted or dried up? What might happen to the plants and the animals? Which ones could survive and how?

Use card to make mobiles of the food chains, using pictures of the plants and animals as well as their names.

Suggestion(s) for extension

Visit a pond to observe the plants and animals at first hand. Use nets to dredge the bottom, middle and surface of the water. Look at the plants and animals found at each level. What differences are there? Are certain plants and animals only found in particular areas of the pond? Why? Can feeding be observed? Draw food chains observed at the pond.

Suggestions(s) for support

Prepare lists of what animals eat: 'These animals eat insects', 'These eat plants', 'These eat worms', and so on. The children could use these lists rather than reference books to prepare their food chains. Alternatively, ask each child to find out what just one or two animals eat. Then come together as a group to share information and make a group food chain.

Opportunities for IT

Children could show food chains using a simple graphics package. The text can be set in different sizes appropriate to each link as the chain progresses, and the links can be drawn with lines. Children might be able to draw the animals and plants in the chain or use pictures from clip art collections. Alternatively, they could scan in their own drawings.

LIFE PROCESSES AND LIVING THINGS

Display ideas
Make a wall collage of a pond, showing the animals and plants that live there. Hang the food chain mobiles in front of the mural.

Reference to photocopiable sheet
Pair up good readers with poorer readers if necessary. The children can use the back of the sheet to write out more pond food chains.

FOOD CHAINS (2)

Nearly all food chains start with a green plant.
†† *Whole class or large groups.*
🕑 *30–45 minutes.*

Previous skills/knowledge needed
Food chains show feeding relationships between living things.

Key background information
Green plants are the only living things which can produce their own food. They manufacture it in their leaves by a process called photosynthesis. They provide food and oxygen for other living things, and thus nearly all food chains begin with green plants.

Preparation
Make some large labels with these words on them: pike, rudd, water flea, fox, rabbit, badger, earthworm, barn owl, vole, heron, roach, water beetle, pond snail, buzzard, mouse, peregrine falcon, pigeon, human, deer, algae (two labels), grain (two labels), grass (four labels), plant remains.

Resources needed
Labels, safety pins, paper, felt-tipped pens, pencils, a large open space, pictures of the animals named on the labels (if possible).

What to do
This activity requires a large open space. Pin one of the labels on each child, then ask the children to sit down in a circle. Explain that they are going to play a game about food chains.

Ask them to tell you what a food chain is and to give you some examples. Do the children know anything about the animals on their labels? If possible, show pictures of what the animals look like. Do the children know what they eat? Discuss the things some of the animals can eat. Talk about the plants also. What are 'algae'? What are 'grains'? Use a large sheet of paper to draw some food chains involving the named plants and animals. What do the children notice about these food chains? What is the one thing which is common to all of them? Discuss how important plants are: they provide food for all other living things.

Explain to the children that they are now going to play a food chain game. Tell the children to stand. Place the 'plants' around the area in a fixed position. Tell them that they cannot move! The 'animals' are then set free to 'hunt'. (Of course, they are only allowed to hunt prey that these animals would eat in real life.) Once an animal has been caught by another, the two children must join hands and then go together to a plant which they think the smaller animal eats. The first children to make a food chain with a plant win. Check the chains that have been made. Are they correct? The game can be played several times, and the children can exchange labels so that they all get a turn at being an animal or a plant. Once the children know how to join three things in a chain,

they could try to join four or five. Who can make the first complete chain?

Possible food chains using these labels include:

> algae → water flea → rudd → pike
> grass → rabbit → fox
> plant remains → earthworm → badger
> grass → vole → barn owl
> algae → pond snail → water beetle → roach → heron
> grain → mouse → buzzard
> grain → pigeon → peregrine falcon
> grass → deer → human

The children could then go on to draw and label the food chains made in the game.

Suggestion(s) for extension
Find out more about the terms *producer*, *consumer* and *decomposer*. What role does each of these play? Make lists of the living things in each group. Investigate how they all interrelate. Find out about *food webs*.

Suggestion(s) for support
If the children do not know what some of the animals eat, tell them. Draw up all the possible food chains using the animal and plant labels. This will enable the children to know exactly what animal(s) to hunt during the game. The children could then illustrate the food chains drawn by the teacher.

Display ideas
Make jigsaw food chains using pictures or words on cards. Place the cards on a table with a sign challenging the children to make up the food chains. Make mobiles of food chains. Make a wall collage with plants in the centre, surrounded by pictures of animals. Join up the items in a food chain with ribbon or string.

MICRO-ORGANISMS

Micro-organisms can be beneficial or harmful.
†† *Small groups. Whole-class discussion.*
🕐 *30–45 minutes plus daily observations of 5–10 minutes.*

Previous skills/knowledge needed
There is a huge variety of living things.

Key background information
Micro-organisms are living things which are so small, we cannot see them without a microscope. They can be both beneficial and harmful. Some micro-organisms can cause disease. We pick up micro-organisms every time we touch things. This is why it is important for us to wash our hands

before eating. Helpful micro-organisms include those which help in the breakdown of waste materials. This helps to return nutrients to the environment, which in turn provides food for other living things.

Preparation
Purchase some bread and cheese. Access to a fridge is also required.

Resources needed
Eight clean plastic jars with lids or plastic food bags with ties, sticky labels, pens, cheese, bread, a knife, a fridge, hand-lenses, paper.

What to do
Provide each group with eight jars or plastic bags, eight sticky labels, four chunks of cheese and four slices of bread. Explain that they are going to find out what happens to food if it is

left uneaten for several weeks. Tell the children to wash their hands before handling the first pieces of cheese and bread. Take three pieces of cheese and three pieces of bread and place a piece of each in a separate container. Attach the appropriate label to each container: 'Cheese – clean hands' or 'Bread – clean hands'. Now tell the children to take the last piece of cheese and bread. They then touch the floor with their hands, and then use their hands to put the piece of cheese and the piece of bread into separate containers. These can be labelled 'Cheese – dirty hands' and 'Bread – dirty hands'. Keep both 'dirty hands' samples and one of each of the 'clean hands' samples at room temperature. Store

·LIFE PROCESSES
AND LIVING THINGS

one of each of the other 'clean hands' food samples (both bread and cheese) in the fridge, and one sample of each in a warm place.

Ask the children to predict what might happen to the food in each case. Can they give reasons why? Allow the children time each day to observe the food over several weeks. Encourage them to record what is happening in some way. What changes are occurring? Are there changes in colour, shape and texture? Is anything growing on the food? Let them use the hand-lenses to look more closely at the food through the containers, but do not allow them to open the containers or touch the food with their hands.

After several weeks have passed, discuss the experiment with the whole class. Did everyone obtain similar results? Were their results expected? Discuss the differences between the food samples touched with clean hands and those touched with dirty hands. What does this tell us? Why is personal hygiene important? Were there any differences between the food samples kept at room temperature and those kept in a warmer place? Why are the fridge results different from these? What does this tell us about storing food at home? Discuss the benefits and harmful effects of food decomposition with the children. Talk about getting rid of food wastes at home. Can it be turned into something useful? What are the possible dangers of eating foods which have been stored for a long time?

Talk about other micro-organisms which cannot be seen with the naked eye – for example, germs which cause diseases. (Strictly speaking, whereas *bacteria* – such as those which cause sore throats – are living micro-organisms, *viruses* – such as those which cause 'flu – are only fragments of genetic material coated in protein. But both can be infectious and cause diseases, and are thus 'germs'.)

Compare this activity with what happens to plants and animals in the environment. What happens to animals and plants that die? What other living things can benefit from this process?

Suggestion(s) for extension
Make compost from household and garden waste. Find out more about bacteria, moulds and fungi. The children could test samples of bread and cheese with 'dirty hands' at colder and warmer temperatures.

Suggestion(s) for support
Act as scribe, if necessary, when recording the results of the experiment. Ask questions to help the children observe what is happening to the food more closely: Has it changed colour? Has it changed shape? Can you see anything growing on it? What do you think this is? Where do you think it came from? Is the piece of food getting smaller? Why?

Assessment opportunities
This activity will enable you to assess how well the child can record observations. Does the child use tables or graphs to represent what she has observed? Does the child use these results to draw conclusions?

Display ideas
Take photographs of the food every week to show the stages of decomposition. Display these, together with the children's own observational notes and drawings of what happened. Make posters about how to avoid spreading germs.

Other aspects of the Science PoS covered
Experimental and Investigative Science – 1b; 2a, b; 3a, c, d, e.

Plants

The activities in this section of the book encourage children to explore the characteristics, functions and life cycles of plants. In the course of carrying out the activities, the children will gain experience in questioning, observing, predicting, recording, measuring and drawing conclusions. They will also have opportunities to work co-operatively and to share their ideas with others.

The activities will provide opportunities for the children to find out about the parts of plants and their functions, how plants survive in their environment and how keys can be used to identify plants. The children will discover the importance of green plants to the environment and how they provide food for other living things.

LIFE PROCESSES
AND LIVINGTHINGS

PLANT VARIETY

There is a huge variety of different plants.

†† *Small groups or pairs.*

⏱ *45–60 minutes.*

⚠ *Beware of poisonous or harmful plants and wash hands after handling specimens.*

Previous skills/knowledge needed

Plants are living things.

Key background information

Plants show nearly as great a range of diversity as animals. Some plants have seeds (flowering plants and conifers), and some do not (ferns, mosses, liverworts, lichens, fungi and algae).

Preparation

Duplicate the required number of copies of photocopiable pages 122 and 123 (one per child). Cut up some small pieces of card and colour each piece a different shade of green, brown or yellow. Select a suitable walk in, or near, the school grounds which will provide the children with a chance to observe many different types of plants. Obtain permission to carry out the walk if necessary. Ensure that there are enough adult helpers to accompany you on the walk, and that the children have suitable clothing.

Resources needed

Photocopiable pages 122 and 123, pencils, plastic bags, hand-lenses, clipboards, plant identification books, coloured pieces of card, measuring tapes, rulers, adhesive tape.

What to do

Divide the class into pairs or small groups for the walk. Discuss safety considerations and agree on a code of behaviour for the walk – walk quietly, do not damage too many plants, collect only very small samples, put back things as they were found, and so on. Hand out the photocopiable sheets and explain how to fill them in. The children can use adhesive tape to fix small specimens to their 'I-Spy' sheets.

Give a coloured piece of card to each child and ask them to try to find that colour in the plants they see on the walk. Can all the colours be matched up? The children can use the 'I-Spy' sheets as they go along. Encourage them to stop every now and then to look more closely at the plants around them. What differences and similarities can they note? Do different plants grow in sunny places and shady places? How many small/medium/large plants can they see?

Can the children find some lichen or moss? Where do these plants grow? Use the hand-lenses to look at them more closely. How do they compare with other plants? What is different about them? What is the same? (*Safety note* – If you find fungi, it is best not to touch them as some are poisonous. Instead, take photographs or ask the children to draw what they see.)

Ask the children to make a detailed study of a particular plant, using photocopiable page 123. The children can use the plastic bags to take away small samples of leaves,

LIFE PROCESSES AND LIVINGTHINGS

bark, twigs and so on. Take loose specimens from the ground whenever possible, rather than picking from live plants.

Once back at school, ask the children to share what they have seen and discovered. How many different types of plants were seen? What differences in colours, shapes, sizes, textures were there? What was the least common? What was the most common (greatest number of samples)? How much do leaf sizes vary? Were all plants green? Record their findings on a large chart.

Suggestion(s) for extension
Use the collection of leaves, bark and twigs for sorting activities. Working in pairs or groups, the children can sort their own collection in some way and then ask others to work out what criterion they have used for sorting.

Suggestion(s) for support
Use a variety of house plants to look at differences and similarities between plants before the walk. This will give the child practice in looking at colours, shapes, sizes, textures and so on. Act as scribe if necessary when the children are completing the 'My plant' sheet, or pair off able writers with less able writers.

Display ideas
Make a large ABC of plant names. Display the children's drawings of and notes about the plants seen on the walk, together with any photographs taken. Make huge three-dimensional models of plants and trees to serve as a background to the work. Display a collection of house plants alongside the children's observational drawings and paintings.

Other aspects of the Science PoS covered
Experimental and Investigative Science – 2a, b; 3b.

Reference to photocopiable sheets
Page 122 – the children can work individually or in pairs for this activity. They could draw, write about, make rubbings of or collect samples of each plant they find.
Page 123 – this is a more detailed study of an individual plant.

SORTING PLANTS
Plants can be sorted into groups.
†† *Whole-class activity.*
🕐 *45–60 minutes.*

Previous skills/knowledge needed
There are differences and similarities between living things.

Key background information
Scientists have sorted plants into several main groups: *angiosperms* (seed-bearing flowers), *gymnosperms* (conifers), ferns, mosses, liverworts, algae, fungi and lichens.

Preparation
Obtain a wide variety of house plants with different leaf shapes and colours, with different flowers, in different sizes and so on. The use of a large area where all the children can sit in a circle is required.

Resources needed
House plants, paper, pencils, a felt-tipped pen.

What to do
Arrange the children into a circle with the house plants in the middle. Have some paper and a felt-tipped pen at hand. Explain to the children that they are going to look for similarities between the plants and use these features to link the plants together in a chain. Start off by writing the words 'has pointed leaves' (or something else which relates to the collection) on a piece of paper with the felt-tipped pen. Place the paper next to a plant which has pointed leaves. Then ask the children to find another plant which has pointed leaves and to place this on the other side of the label.

Now challenge the children to think of a different thing that the plant they chose has in common with another plant in the collection. When someone finds a similarity, they can write it on the paper and add the plant to the line. And so it goes on, until all of the plants are joined together in a line or a circle (with a different similarity used each time). Examples of possible joining words might include: 'has round leaves', 'small', 'tall', 'has white flowers', 'shiny leaves', 'rough leaves', 'tall stem', 'large petals', 'small petals'.

The activity can be adapted to incorporate specific differences between the plants. These sorting games help the children to become more familiar with the plant collection, and are a good way of sharing ideas about the similarities and differences that can be found.

Next, ask the children to sort the plants into groups in some way. Ask individual children to do the sorting and then to see if the others can guess the criterion used for the sort. Try out three or four sorting criteria from the whole group and then ask the children to draw a record of a sort, using their own idea or one that has been tried. Discuss their

results. In how many different ways can the collection be grouped? Consider less obvious ways by looking at the plant labels and sorting plants into groups that require lots of water, lots of shade, and so on.

Suggestion(s) for extension
Find out about the different plant groups which scientists use for classification. Sort the plants seen on a walk (see previous activity) into these groups.

Suggestion(s) for support
Help those children who experience difficulties in sorting by asking questions, such as: Are the leaves all one colour? Do some of the plants have flowers? Are the stems the same? What shapes are the leaves? Are some of the plants taller than others? Do any have a smell? Are some leaves smooth? What are the leaf edges like?

Assessment opportunities
The children's individual drawings of, or writing about, how they sorted the plants can be kept as evidence for assessment purposes. This work can then be used to discuss the criteria used in more detail with the child.

Opportunites for IT
This activity can be extended to include the use of a computer branching database to sort plants according to their characteristics.

Display ideas
Put the plants on a table and mount the children's drawings of, and writing about, their sorting on the wall near the table. Add observational drawings and paintings of the plants. Place a selection of reference books near the display to enable children to find out more about the plants and their scientific and/or common names.

Other aspects of the Science PoS covered
Experimental and Investigative Science – 2b, 3b.

PLANT KEYS
Keys can be used to classify plants.
†† *Pairs or small groups. Whole-class or small-group discussion.*
🕐 *30–60 minutes.*

Previous skills/knowledge needed
Plants are living things. Living things can be sorted into groups.

Key background information
Keys are used in science to find out the name of a living thing or the group to which it belongs. Keys can take different forms, but most involve working through a set of questions or descriptions until you find the name or group that best fits the description of what you are trying to identify or classify.

Preparation
Duplicate the required number of copies of photocopiable page 124 (one per child). Obtain a collection of leaves that have different shapes, colours and sizes.

Resources needed
A leaf collection, photocopiable page 124, paper, pencils, scissors, adhesive.

What to do
Provide the children with a collection of leaves. Ask them to note any similarities and differences between them. Encourage the children to compare the leaf shape, texture,

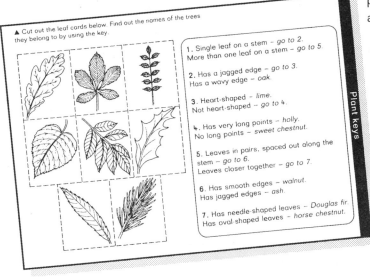

▲ Cut out the leaf cards below. Find out the names of the trees they belong to by using the key.

1. Single leaf on a stem – *go to 2.*
More than one leaf on a stem – *go to 5.*

2. Has a jagged edge – *go to 3.*
Has a wavy edge – *oak.*

3. Heart-shaped – *lime.*
Not heart-shaped – *go to 4.*

4. Has very long points – *holly.*
No long points – *sweet chestnut.*

5. Leaves in pairs, spaced out along the stem – *go to 6.*
Leaves closer together – *go to 7.*

6. Has smooth edges – *walnut.*
Has jagged edges – *ash.*

7. Has needle-shaped leaves – *Douglas fir.*
Has oval-shaped leaves – *horse chestnut.*

Plant keys

colour, veins, leaf edges, size and smell. Then ask them to group the leaves in some way. Can other children work out the criterion for the sorting? How many different ways can the leaves be sorted? Discuss each group's sorting.

Explain that sorting using a special key can help us to find out the name of a plant. Hand out the photocopiable sheet and ask the children to cut out the leaf pictures. Can the children use the key to find out the names of the trees from which the leaves originate? This could be done as a whole-class or group activity to ensure that the children understand how to work through the key correctly. Do the children find the key easy to use?

Explain that there are different types of keys which could be used to identify the leaves (see 'Using keys in the local environment' on page 26). Challenge the children to make up their own keys using the leaf collection. They do not need to name the plants from which the leaves were taken, but the keys should reflect the distinctions between the different leaf types. They could also try to write their own versions of the key on the photocopiable sheet. What additional factors could be introduced to these keys? (Colour, texture, smell, size.) Allow time for the children to try out each other's keys. Are some easier to use than others? Discuss why this is so. When would keys be useful?

Suggestion(s) for extension

Use commercially-produced keys, or the children's own keys, to try to identify plants on a nature walk. Visit several different sites to compare the plants that can be found.

Suggestion(s) for support

Pair up good readers with less able readers.

Assessment opportunities

This activity will enable you to assess how well the children can use identification keys and make up their own ones. The photocopiable sheet could be used as a form of summative assessment at a later date.

Opportunities for IT

Children could extend their work to the use of a branching database on the computer. They will need to 'teach' the database differences between plants by asking questions which have a 'yes/no' answer. The computer then creates a key which can be used by another child to identify any item included within the set of items. The creation of the key is an excellent language development activity. Different groups of children could create their own branching database and try it out with other groups.

Display ideas

Use the children's branching keys to make mobiles.

Mount other types of key on to card and cover them with clear adhesive plastic. Place these on a table with the leaf collection, so that the children can use them.

Other aspects of the Science PoS covered

Experimental and Investigative Science – 2b.

Reference to photocopiable sheet

The easiest way to use this key is to use one leaf picture at a time, and read down through each stage on the key until you find the descriptions that best fit the leaf. The leaf can then be named.

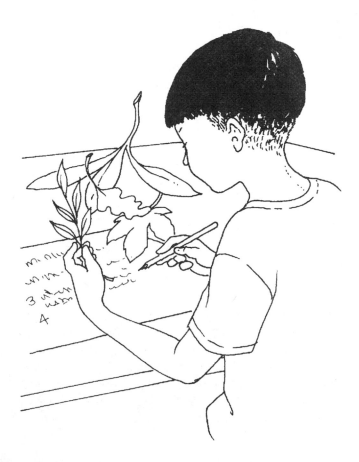

LIFE PROCESSES
AND LIVING THINGS

PLANTS AND WATER

Plants need water to grow.

†† *Pairs or small groups.*

⏲ *Preparation 20–30 minutes. Daily observations 5–20 minutes.*

Previous skills/knowledge needed

Plants are living things.

Key background information

Water is necessary for proper germination of seeds. Plants also need water for growth. However, too much water will rot seeds and can prevent a plant's roots from obtaining enough oxygen.

Preparation

No specific preparation required.

Resources needed

Broad bean seeds, plant pots, saucers, water, a measuring jug, potting soil, adhesive labels, marker pens, rulers, paper, pencils.

What to do

Explain to the children that they are going to find out if plants need water to survive. To do this, they need to plant some bean seeds in separate pots and then see that different pots receive different amounts of water. Discuss the setting up of the experiment. Can the children suggest the things that will need to be kept the same to make the test a fair one? After planting each bean, label the pots: 'no water', '5ml every four days', '10ml every four days', 'water only when soil feels dry', 'soil very wet always'.

Talk to the children about where to place the pots in order to provide the best conditions for the beans to grow. What are their reasons for choosing this spot? Ask them to predict what will happen to each bean and to give a reason for this. Record their reasoning in some way. Water the seeds as per the instructions on the labels. Discuss how they could record the results of the experiment. A daily diary could be kept, or the results could be logged in table form. Allow time each day for watering and recording what happens to the beans. If the bean shoots grow, their height could be measured.

After several weeks, discuss the results of the experiment. What conclusions could be drawn? Which beans grew best? Can the children suggest why? What do they think plants need the water for? Why is too much water as bad as no water at all? Discuss their recording methods. Which methods of recording seemed to work best? How effective was the use of tables or graphs? Was there enough evidence to support their predictions? Did all the groups obtain similar results? Can reasons be given for any difference in outcome? What is the likelihood of the same results being obtained if the experiment were repeated?

Suggestion(s) for extension

Repeat the experiment using different varieties of plants or seeds. Can some plants tolerate more or less water than others?

Suggestion(s) for support

Use a record sheet similar in format to the ones shown on page 90. Help the child to fill out the sheet, acting as scribe if necessary. Discuss how to make the test fair: use the same type of beans, the same amount and type of soil and the same containers, and place them in the same position; the only thing to vary is the amount of water given. Help the children to draw up a table to record the results. Assist with accurate measuring of amounts of water and heights of bean plants. Discuss the results and how they compare with the children's predictions.

LIFE PROCESSES AND LIVINGTHINGS

Assessment opportunities

This activity will provide opportunities for the assessment of accurate measuring and record keeping. It will show how well individual children can use tables and/or graphs for drawing conclusions. The written evidence will provide the teacher with opportunities to discuss the investigation with each child. Comparisons can be made between the predictions and the results, which will assist in determining the child's level of knowledge and understanding.

Opportunities for IT

Children could record their measurements and comments using a spreadsheet, which gives a tabular format for the information as well as providing opportunities to explore the functions of spreadsheets. A different column could be used for each of the watering procedures, and information compared across the columns for each recording date.

	A	B	C	D	E	F
1	Date	no water	5ml /4 days	10ml /4days	when dry	always wet
2	3/10/95					
3	4/10/95					
	Average height					

Alternatively, each group could keep their own spreadsheet and use the extra space to make short comments about the plant growth. At the end of the recording period, the numerical data from several spreadsheets could be combined for analysis by all children.

	A	B	C
1	Date	no water	Comments
2	3/10/95		
3	4/10/95		
	Average height		

If the children have not used spreadsheets before, take some time to explain how they work and what they can do. This can be done with the whole class. Good analogies to use are pigeon-holes and simple map co-ordinates. Show the children how to move around the spreadsheet using either the mouse or the cursor keys, and how they can enter their data into the relevant cells. They will need to know how to save their data on to a disk, and how to retrieve it. Make sure that back-up copies are also kept, or that the spreadsheet is printed out each day.

The easiest approach is for the teacher to call up the spreadsheet for the children, who can take it in turns to enter their data on a daily basis. Once the spreadsheet begins to take shape, formulae can be added to make simple calculations, such as the difference between daily readings or the average height over several days.

Most spreadsheets have graphing facilities to enable line or block graphs to be drawn. If the spreadsheet is extended, several sets of results can be stored on the same spreadsheet for comparative purposes.

Display ideas

Make large paper models to show the results of the bean experiment. Add labels to each pot to say how much water was given to each plant. Include the children's tables, graphs and writing about the experiment.

Other aspects of the Science PoS covered

Experimental and Investigative Science – 1a, b, d; 2a, b, c; 3a, b, c, d. e.

PLANTS AND LIGHT

Plants need sunlight to grow.

†† *Pairs or small groups.*

🕒 *30 minutes to set up. Observation over several weeks.*

Previous skills/knowledge needed

Plants are living things. Plants need water to grow.

Key background information

Green plants need sunlight to manufacture their own food in order to grow. Sunlight, carbon dioxide and water, together with chlorophyll in the leaves, are used to produce oxygen and glucose (a type of sugar). This process is called *photosynthesis*. Photosynthesis does not occur when the plant is in the dark. Because of this, plants tend to grow towards light – this tendency is called *phototropism*. House plants will often lean towards the light from a window. The leaves turn so that each leaf receives the maximum amount of light. Seeds do not need sunlight to grow. They use their own stored energy to provide nourishment for a shoot to grow up through the ground and for roots to grow downwards. Once the shoot has grown above the surface, photosynthesis normally provides the energy required to grow further.

Preparation
No specific preparation required.

Resources needed
Broad bean seeds, plastic drinking cups or yoghurt pots, water, a jug, a dark cupboard, a window ledge or area with plenty of light, potting soil, paper, pencils, marker pens, rulers, a camera (optional).

What to do
Divide the children into pairs or small groups and provide each group with two small plastic containers, two bean seeds, some potting soil and a marker pen. Ask them to fill the pots with the soil and plant the beans about 3cm below the surface. Water each pot. They can then label the pots with their names, using a marker pen.

Explain to the children that they are going to grow some pairs of bean seeds, and that one of each pair will be kept in the light and one in the dark. Both seeds in each pair will need to be watered regularly. Ask the children to predict what will happen to each bean and to write down their ideas. Will both beans grow at the same rate? Will one look different from the other? Why?/Why not?

Then place one pot (for each group of children) near a window and the other in a dark cupboard. Allow the children time in each day to observe their pot and to provide water if the soil becomes dry. Encourage them to record what they see each day. They could measure the height of the plants with a ruler. If possible, take photographs of the seedlings as they grow and note on which dates (and at which times) the photographs were taken.

After several weeks, compare the results of all the groups. Which plants grew the best? Did the plants in the dark grow at all? Did the children predict that this would happen? Why do both plants shoot? Why does one grow better than the other? What differences can be seen between the plant that grew in the dark and the one that grew in the light? Can the children account for these differences? Compare the recording methods used by the different groups. Which ones provide the most information? Which ones are the easiest to understand and use? Discuss any bar graphs, tables or line graphs used. How clear are these? Do they tell us what we want to know? Does the information we have recorded support any of the predictions we made at the beginning? Have we collected enough evidence to show that light is necessary for plant growth? Would we be likely to get the same result if we repeated the experiment?

Suggestion(s) for extension
Ask the children to investigate whether the relative amount of light has any effect on the growth of the bean seedlings. Using the bean seedlings which were grown in the light, set up the following growing conditions: in light all day, in light for five hours a day, in light for two hours a day, in light for one hour a day. Record what happens and ask the children to compare their results.

Suggestion(s) for support
Help those children who cannot devise a recording method of their own or who find recording difficult. Talk about the plant. What colour is it? How tall is it? (Help them to measure it.) How many leaves does it have? What size are the leaves? Is the stem strong or weak? Remind them to water the plant if the soil is dry. Make sure the children do not over-water the plants.

Assessment opportunities
This activity will enable the teacher to assess how well the children can use tables and diagrams to record their observations. They will need to consider their results and compare these with their predictions in order to decide whether the outcome was an expected one or not.

The activity will also give an indication of how accurately the children can use a ruler to measure the plants.

Opportunities for IT

Children could record their measurements using a spreadsheet with columns for date and height data. Formulae could be added to calculate the average daily increase. The spreadsheet can also be used to draw line or bar charts of the plant growth. Written comments could be added in a separate column. Graphing software could also be used to record and represent plant growth over the period.

Children could also use a word processor to make a daily diary of their plant and its response to the light conditions. They could explore ways to format and present the diary to include both measurements and comments.

Display ideas

Use photographs of the bean seedlings and/or the actual plants to make a display showing the differences between plants grown with and without sunlight. Stick a large picture of the sun on the wall behind the display, with words and pictures to show how sunlight helps plants to grow – it helps the leaves to stay green, it makes the stem grow strong, it helps the leaves to grow, it helps to make food for the plant. Also include other information about the things plants need, such as water, nutrients in soil and carbon dioxide (for photosynthesis). If the display is in place for several weeks, encourage the children to observe those plants which were grown in the dark. Do they recover? If so, do they grow as well as the other plants? Again, photographs will help the class to remember what has happened.

Other aspects of the Science PoS covered

Experimental and Investigative Science – 1b, c; 2a, b, c; 3a, b, c, d, e.

PLANTS AND NUTRIENTS

Plants need nutrients (minerals) to grow.

†† *Pairs or small groups.*

🕐 *30–40 minutes preparation. 5–10 minutes daily observation.*

⚠ *Make sure the children wash their hands after handling soil samples.*

Previous skills/knowledge needed

Plants are living things. Plants need sunlight and water to grow.

Key background information

Green plants have the ability to make their own food from particular raw materials found in the environment: water from the soil and carbon dioxide from the air. Other raw materials which plants need for healthy growth can be found in the soil. Raw materials (*mineral salts*) obtained from the soil include compounds of nitrogen, sulphur, phosphorus, potassium, calcium, magnesium and traces of iron, boron, molybdenum, zinc and copper. Plants do not necessarily need soil to survive – as long as they receive the nutrients they require, they will be able to grow. *Hydroponics* is the science of growing plants without soil: the nutrients the plants need are added to the water they receive, and the plant is rooted not in soil but in gravel or coarse sand.

Preparation

Obtain some broad bean seeds and a range of growing mediums such as soils, sand, potting compost and so on.

Resources needed

Broad bean seeds, plant pots with saucers or yoghurt pots, different soils, potting compost, sand, sawdust, blotting paper, cotton wool, cloth, water, a measuring jug, a ruler, paper, pencils, adhesive labels.

What to do

Challenge the children to investigate which potting materials are the best for plant growth. Talk about ways to ensure the testing is fair. What things will need to be kept the same? (Type of pot, amount of water, type of bean, depth to which bean is planted, position of pot in the room.) What will need to be different in each pot? (The growing medium.)

Provide various growing mediums (sand, soil, potting compost, sawdust, cotton wool, cloth, and so on), but allow the children to select other mediums if they wish. Make sure they label each pot with the name of the medium, the date of planting and the names of the children in the group.

Encourage the children to make predictions about what they think will happen in each case and to give reasons why it will occur. How will they decide which plant grows the 'best'? Is it the one which grows the tallest? The one which looks the healthiest? The one with the most leaves? How long will they need to continue the investigation before a decision can be made? The answers to these questions may not be apparent at the outset, but they will require consideration as the investigation unfolds.

Discuss how the results will be recorded. Will the children devise their own methods or will a set record sheet (similar in format to those shown on page 90) be used?

After the investigation has been completed, discuss the results with the whole class. What conclusions can be drawn? Were the results expected? How well did the children's predictions match the results? Are water and sunlight alone sufficient for plants to grow? Has enough evidence been obtained to answer this question? How likely is it that the same results would be obtained if the experiment were repeated? Do the plants take in any nutrients from the soil? How are these absorbed?

Suggestion(s) for extension

Use a database computer program to collate the results from all the groups. Use the program to find relationships, for example between the height of the plant and the growing medium.

Suggestion(s) for support

Help the children to complete their record sheets. Act as scribe if necessary. Help to measure the plants and record the results. Talk about what could be noted during the investigation. Are the colours of the plants different? Are their heights different? Do some leaves look healthier than others? Are the stems all the same thickness? Do some plants have more leaves? Do some plants stand up more

easily? Discuss why this might be so – soil helps to support the plant, the soil contains nutrients the plant needs.

Assessment opportunities

This activity provides an opportunity for the teacher to observe the children's ability to carry out an investigation themselves. It will allow aspects of AT1 as well as AT2 to be assessed.

Opportunities for IT

Children, or the teacher, could create a simple spreadsheet with columns for each group/growing medium. Each row would be a date. Children could enter their measurements over a period of time, saving and retrieving their data on each occasion. The spreadsheet would enable comparisons to be made between growth in different mediums, as well as some statistical work on daily, average and total growth. Graphs could also be drawn plotting height against the date for each growing medium.

Display ideas

Ask the children to set up their own displays to show their investigations with information on how they set up the experiments, what they thought would happen and the final results. Allow the children to select their own materials for backing and mounting the displays. Ask them to evaluate the displays once they are finished. What could they have done better? What do they like about the displays?

Other aspects of the Science PoS covered

Experimental and Investigative Science – 1a, b, c, d, e; 2a, b, c, 3a, b, c, d, e.

PLANTS AND TEMPERATURE

Temperature affects plant growth.

†† *Pairs or small groups.*

🕐 *30 minutes preparation. 5–10 minutes daily observation.*

Previous skills/knowledge needed
Plants are living things. Seeds need water to germinate.

Key background information
Different plants are adapted to grow at different temperatures. Arctic plants can survive in conditions that would kill plants from warmer regions. Many desert plants have hairy leaves or shiny surfaces. These help to reduce the temperature of the leaves by reflecting more light from them (leaf hairs keep the leaf surface in the shade – as hair protects the human head). Many desert plant leaves are narrow and pointed. This can help to increase heat loss by convection. Temperature can affect seed germination.

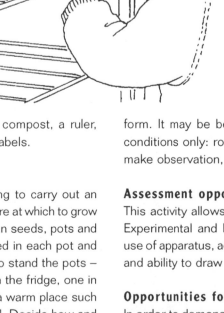

Preparation
Obtain access to a fridge-freezer.

Resources needed
Plant pots or yoghurt pots, broad bean seeds, a fridge-freezer, water, a measuring jug, potting compost, a ruler, paper, pencils, a thermometer, adhesive labels.

What to do
Explain to the children that they are going to carry out an experiment to discover the best temperature at which to grow bean seeds. Provide each group with bean seeds, pots and potting compost. Tell them to plant a seed in each pot and then to water the seed. Discuss places to stand the pots – one could be placed in the freezer, one in the fridge, one in the middle of the classroom, and one in a warm place such as near a heater or on a sunny windowsill. Decide how and when to water the seeds. Should they be given the same amount of water each day, or only be watered when the soil feels dry? Ask the children to label each pot with its date of planting, its position and the names of the children in the group.

Can they predict what will happen to each bean and give their reasons? Discuss the role of light in this experiment. Seeds will germinate without light, as they use the store of food inside the seed to grow a root and a shoot. Once shooted, however, the plants need light; so this experiment will focus on whether the seeds will germinate, not on how well the plant will grow afterwards (as the seeds in the fridge and freezer do not have access to light).

Ask the children how they will record their results. (Record sheets similar to those shown on page 90 could be used.) Allow them time each day to observe what has happened to their seeds. They could use a thermometer to record the temperature of the spot in which the beans are placed.

After a week or so, discuss the results with the whole class. Did the results support their predictions? Did some seeds germinate faster than others? Why? Could other factors besides temperature affect the seeds? Did all the groups obtain similar results? What factors may have been responsible for differences in results?

Suggestion(s) for extension
Try the same experiment using different seeds. Compare results with bean seeds.

Suggestion(s) for support
You may need to help the children with recording or act as scribe. Help the children to use a thermometer correctly. Daily observations could be recorded on tape rather than in written form. It may be better for some children to consider two conditions only: room temperature and in a fridge. This will make observation, measuring and recording easier.

Assessment opportunities
This activity allows the teacher to assess some aspects of Experimental and Investigative Science: use of prediction, use of apparatus, accuracy of measurements, recording skills and ability to draw conclusions.

Opportunities for IT
In order to demonstrate to children how the temperatures in each location may fluctuate, a temperature sensor could be linked to the computer and the temperature recorded over 24 hours. This could be set up in each location in turn, so that each group understands how the growth of plants may be affected by the changes in temperature. The data-logging

software can plot graphs of the changes in temperature, which can then be printed out.

Each group could record their results using a graphing program or a spreadsheet. If a spreadsheet is used, several sets of results can be kept on the same spreadsheet and comparisons made between the rates of growth. Some statistical analysis of daily, average and total growth can also be made.

Display ideas

Make a large card thermometer. Make small drawings of plants which can survive at high, moderate and low temperatures, then place these at the appropriate points alongside the thermometer and mount them on the wall. Add the children's own observational drawings of, and notes about, the bean seed experiment.

Other aspects of the Science PoS covered

Experimental and Investigative Science – 1a, b, c, d, e; 2a, b, c; 3a, b, c, d, e.

MOVEMENT IN PLANTS

Plants are capable of movement.

†† *Pairs or small groups.*

🕐 *30–45 minutes. Daily observations over several weeks.*

⚠ *Use of the craft knife should be supervised by the teacher.*

Previous skills/knowledge needed

Plants are living things. Plants need water and light to grow.

Key background information

Plants are capable of movement. This movement is usually not as obvious as in animals, but plants can respond to several stimuli which cause them to move. Some plants, such as the mimosa, can alter the position of their leaves rapidly when touched. Most plants can respond to light. The bending of a shoot or root tip is an example of *tropism* or directional growth. When light causes this bending, it is called *phototropism*.

Preparation

No specific preparation required.

Resources needed

Cress seeds, two saucers, cotton wool, water, a shoe box, a craft knife, paper, pencils.

What to do

Talk to the children about movement in plants. What can cause plants to move? Discuss the effects of wind and

growth. Some children may already be aware of the way plants grow towards sunlight. To demonstrate this, talk about house plants and how they often lean towards the light. Why is this? Explain that the children are going to investigate how plants are able to change the direction of their growth in response to light.

Soak some cotton wool in water and press it into the saucers to create a level surface. Sprinkle some cress seeds on the cotton wool. Cut a small hole (about the size of a 1p coin) in one side of the shoe box. Place the saucers in a sunny position, perhaps on a window ledge, and then place the shoe box upside-down over one saucer. Ask the children to predict what will happen to the seedlings in both saucers. Can they give their reasons for thinking this?

Allow the children time each day to ensure that the cotton wool stays moist and to check the growth of the seeds. Encourage them to record what happens in some way. After the seeds have shooted and grown towards the hole in the box, cover the hole up and cut a new hole in another side, or turn the box around so that the hole is facing a different way. (Make sure that the sunlight will still reach the hole in the box.) Can the children say what will happen to the seedlings inside the box now? Again, allow them time to observe what is happening each day and to record what they see.

Were the results expected? Why is there a difference between the ways the plants grew on the two saucers? Why did we need to have two saucers? Why do plants bend towards the light source? How could this help them to survive in the wild?

LIFE PROCESSES AND LIVINGTHINGS

Suggestion(s) for extension
Find out about other response mechanisms, for example in insectivorous plants such as the Venus fly-trap.

Suggestion(s) for support
Act as scribe if necessary to assist recording, or take photographs to help demonstrate what has happened. Use record sheets like those shown on page 90, if necessary.

Assessment opportunities
This activity will allow the teacher to assess some aspects of Experimental and Investigative Science – for example, how well the children can record and draw conclusions.

Opportunities for IT
Children could word-process their notes to form part of a class display or book.

Display ideas
Draw large pictures of the seedling growth from Day One onwards. Ask the children to write sentences about what is happening in each picture. Mount these on the wall or use them to make a class book.

Other aspects of the Science PoS covered
Experimental and Investigative Science – 1a, b, c, d, e; 2b, c; 3a, b, c, d, e.

Preparation
No specific preparation required.

Resources needed
Cress or bean seeds, blotting paper or cotton wool, clear containers, water, baby spider plants, carrots, a knife, hand-lenses, a microscope (optional), paper, pencils, a potted plant (such as a spider plant).

What to do
Remove a potted plant from its container and show it to the group. Can they name the plant parts? Look at the roots more carefully. Is there one main root? Can the root hairs be seen? How many secondary roots are there? Use the hand-lenses to look more closely. What else can the children notice about the roots? Do they know what the roots are used for in a plant? Have they seen the roots of trees and other plants? What do these look like? Why do they think tree roots go down for such a long way? Is the size of the roots related to the size of the plant?

Next, look at some carrots with their tops on. Ask the children to name the plant parts. Which is the root? Look more closely at this part of the plant. Are there root hairs? What purpose do these have? Slice off a piece of carrot. Look at the central core. What purpose would this have? Then cut the carrot lengthways and look at the central core.

ROOTS

Roots have a particular function in plants.

†† *Small groups.*

🕐 *30–45 minutes for the activity. 5–10 minutes daily observation.*

⚠ *Use of the knife should be supervised by the teacher.*

Previous skills/knowledge needed
Plants are living things. Plants require sunlight, water and certain minerals to grow.

Key background information
The roots of a plant have two functions: they anchor the plant and they take in water and nutrients. The roots require moisture to grow. There are two main types of root: *tap roots* and *fibrous roots*. A tap root system consists of a main or tap root which grows straight down and several other secondary roots which grow out from the tap root. A fibrous root system consists of a mass of roots of roughly the same length. The roots have tiny *root hairs* which increase the surface area of the root and thus increase the amount of water and nutrients taken in. Carrots, turnips and similar plants have large tap roots in which food is stored. Not all roots grow underground.

Explain that the water and minerals are transported along this core. In a fresh carrot, water will appear inside the carrot when cut. If possible, use a microscope to look more closely at a root hair or a very thin slice of root.

Next, try growing some seedlings and plants to observe the development of roots. Put some blotting paper or cotton wool inside a clear container, and place the cress or bean seeds between the paper and the wall of the container. Keep the paper damp. The stages of germination can then be clearly observed. Ask the children to make daily observational drawings and notes of what happens.

'Baby' spider plants are ideal for propagation. Place some baby plants in jars of water and observe the root growth. How long do the roots take to appear? What do they look like? Do all the roots on one plant look the same? Can root hairs be seen? Plant the baby spider plants in soil after the roots have appeared, and grow some new plants.

Suggestion(s) for extension
Grow some bean seeds using clear containers and blotting paper as described above, but this time place the seeds in different positions: level, at an angle, and so on. Watch the seeds growing. Which way do the roots grow? Does it matter which way round the seed is planted?

Suggestion(s) for support
Help the children with the recording or act as scribe if necessary, or pair up more able writers with less able writers.

Assessment opportunities
This activity will enable the teacher to assess the children's ability to record their observations in a clear and orderly way.

Opportunities for IT
Pupils could make their daily observational notes using a word processor. This would involve retrieving and saving their 'diary' each time they add information to it.

Display ideas
Make a display of plants whose roots we eat, such as carrots, parsnips, radishes, turnips and beetroot. Mount pictures of plants, such as large trees and aquatic plants, on the wall and include their roots. Add the children's observational drawings of, and notes about, growing seeds and spider plants. Draw a large root system of a plant and label the root parts. Make labels to say what the functions of roots are. Make flip books to show the growth of roots in the bean or cress seedlings.

Other aspects of the Science PoS covered
Experimental and Investigative Science – 2a, b; 3b.

STEMS

The stem has a particular function in plants.
†† *Pairs or small groups.*
🕐 *30–45 minutes. Observations: morning and afternoon over several days.*
⚠ *Use of the knife should be supervised by the teacher.*

Previous skills/knowledge needed
Plants are living things. Plants need water, light and certain minerals to help them grow.

Key background information
The stems of plants have several functions: to conduct water and minerals from the roots to the leaves; to conduct food, manufactured in the leaves, to other parts of the plant; to produce and support the leaves; and to produce and support the flowers and fruit. Some stems are modified to act as food stores. These are called *corms* and *rhizomes*, such as those of the crocus and iris. The potato is a modified underground stem, known as a *stem tuber*. (Similarly modified roots, or *root tubers*, are found in dahlias and other plants.)

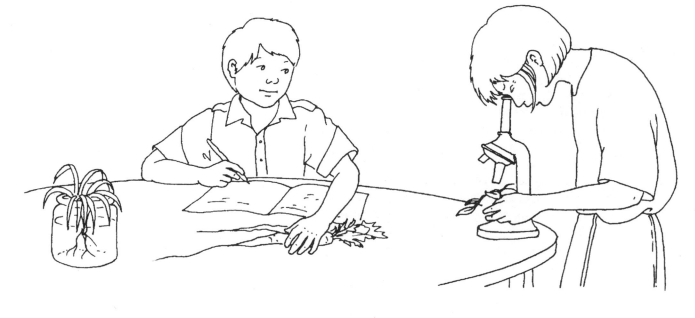

**LIFE PROCESSES
AND LIVING THINGS**

Fine tubes run through the roots, stem and leaves, and water is pulled into these tubes by capillary action (in the way that sponges soak up water). There are two stem types: *herbaceous* and *woody*. Herbaceous stems are common in annual plants. They are usually soft and green, and do not increase much in diameter during the life of the plant. Woody stems, however, do increase in diameter, and are hard with an outer covering of bark.

Preparation

Obtain some plants with different types of stems – woody and herbaceous; also some celery with leaves or some white carnations (or other white flowers).

Resources needed

Plants (as above), four jars (all of the same size), food colouring and/or ink, water, a measuring jug, a knife, paper, pencils, hand-lenses, a paper towel, coloured tape (or a marker pen), scissors.

What to do

Provide the children with a collection of different plants. Ask them to look at the stems of the plants. What similarities and differences can they see between them? Encourage the children to feel and smell the stems, and let them use the hand-lenses to examine the stems more closely. What colours are they? What are their textures? Is anything growing from the stems? How are the leaves arranged on the stem? Can the children suggest why this might be?

Discuss the purposes of the stems. Can the children suggest reasons why plants have stems? Why are the stems different on different plants? Why are tree stems much stronger and larger? Look at nodes and buds on the stems, and discuss how leaves grow from the stems. Why are the leaves not all on one side of the stem? Ask the children to do some observational drawings of the different stems.

Cut open some stems of flowers and other plants. What can be seen inside? Why are the stems watery inside? Where has the water come from? Why do plants need water?

Explain to the children that they are going to investigate one of the functions of a plant stem. Cut the ends off the stems of four celery sticks (with leaves) or four carnations, and place each plant in its own clear jar. Add a measured

amount of water to each jar (about one-third full). Then add several drops of food colouring and/or ink to two of the jars. Use coloured tape or a marker pen to mark the water level in each jar (make sure they are all at the same level). Place two jars (one with coloured water and one with plain water) in a warm place, perhaps near a heater or in a sunny position. Place the other two jars in a cool place. Ask the children to say what they think will happen to the plants in each case. Can they give their reasons? Discuss the use of a *control* – that is, the plants in plain water. Allow the children time to observe the plants every morning and afternoon over several days, in order to note what is happening.

The petals of the flowers or the leaves of the celery should become tinged with the food colouring/ink. Cut open the stems to look at the colouring inside. How far up the stem has the colouring travelled? Compare these stems with the stems of the plants in plain water. Explain that the water travels up tubes in the stem in the same way that a paper towel soaks up water. Demonstrate this with some paper towels and water.

How much water have the plants taken up? Measure the height of water left in the jars to find out. Compare the amounts of water used up by the plants in a warm place with the amounts of water used up by those in a cool place. Is there a difference? Why might this be? Could some water have disappeared from the jars in other ways? How? Discuss evaporation. How could evaporation be prevented/reduced? Could something be put on/over the water surface? Discuss and investigate this.

Suggestion(s) for extension

Find out about growth rings in trees, and the different parts of a plant stem – epidermis, vascular bundles and pith. Visit different local sites to observe the stems of different plants. How different are the stems of water plants from those of land plants? Why?

Suggestion(s) for support

Help the children to record what is happening, acting as scribe if necessary. Assist with water measurements. Supervise

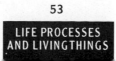

the cutting of the stems. Ask questions such as: How do you think the water might get inside the plant? How do you think it might travel up the stem? Why doesn't the water stop moving when the stem is 'full' of water? Where does the water go to? Why does the plant need water? Why have we put food colouring in the water? How will this help us to see where the water went?

Display ideas
Display a collection of woody stems and of herbaceous plants with different stems. Mount the children's observational drawings, along with the results from the experiment, on the wall. Add information about the functions of plant stems.

Other aspects of the Science PoS covered
Experimental and Investigative Science – 1b; 2a, b, c; 3c.

LEAVES

The leaf has a particular function in plants.
†† *Small groups.*
⏱ *45–60 minutes.*
⚠ *Handling of plastic bags must be supervised by the teacher.*

Previous skills/knowledge needed
Plants are living things. Plant stems and roots have particular functions.

Key background information
Most leaves consist of a flat blade and a stalk which connects it to the stem. Leaves come in a huge variety of shapes and sizes. There are two main types: *simple* and *compound*. A simple leaf has one blade attached to the stalk, whereas a compound leaf has two or more leaflets on one stalk. The main function of the leaves in green plants is to produce food through photosynthesis: a type of sugar is produced from carbon dioxide and water in the presence of sunlight and chlorophyll in the leaves. Oxygen is a waste by-product of this process, and passes out through the leaves of the plant. Leaves are also important because they allow the plant to lose water and thus maintain the flow of *transpiration*. Water escapes from the leaves and turns into water vapour.

Preparation
Obtain a collection of leaves of different sizes, colours and shapes, and a variety of different house plants.

Resources needed
A collection of leaves and house plants, hand-lenses, paper, pencils, a small house plant such as the goose-foot plant, plastic bags (large enough to cover a plant), rulers.

What to do
Show the collection of plants to the group. Ask them to look for similarities and differences between the leaves of different plants. What differences in colour, shape, size, texture and the number and positions of leaves do they notice? Are the leaves on one plant all the same? In what ways do they vary? Are young leaves the same as older leaves?

Look at the collection of separate leaves next. Allow the children time to observe them closely using hand-lenses. What do they notice about the veins, leaf edges, length of stalk, surface of the leaves, and so on? Is one type of leaf edge most common? Do the top and bottom surfaces of the same leaf feel or look different? Discuss simple and compound leaves. Can the children sort the leaves into these

two groups? Measure the leaves. What differences are there in size? Make rubbings of the leaves. Can other children match the rubbings to the original leaves? What distinguishing features does each leaf have? Do desert plants, such as cacti, have different leaves from those of other plants? Why might this be? Ask the children to make observational drawings of the leaves.

Discuss the functions of the leaves with the children. Why do they think a plant has leaves? Why are the leaves attached to the stem at different places? Do the leaves of a plant all face in the same direction? Explain to the children that the leaves of green plants are very important because they make food for the rest of the plant. The leaves contain a special chemical called *chlorophyll* which makes them green. The chlorophyll helps in the food-making process called *photosynthesis*. Plants use carbon dioxide from the air, water from the soil and sunlight to produce a type of sugar. Oxygen is released in this process. Talk about how humans and animals convert oxygen from the air into carbon dioxide during respiration, and explain that in this way plants and animals depend on each other to live. (Plants also respire, but consume less oxygen in respiration than they produce during photosynthesis. Animals produce no oxygen; they only consume it.) Discuss how the sugar produced during photosynthesis is transported around the plant in the stem. How similar is this to the way that our blood is transported in our veins and arteries?

Explain that the leaves have another important role, and that the children are going to carry out a simple investigation to find out what this is. Completely cover a watered, small house plant such as a goose-foot plant with a clear plastic bag, making sure there are no holes through which air can pass. Place the plant in a sunny position. Can the children suggest what might happen? Can they give their reasons? Leave the plant overnight or for several days, and then discuss what has happened. Why is there water in the bag? Why might the plant need to lose water? Where do they think the water escapes from? Why does it condense on the inside of the bag? Talk about evaporation and water vapour. Explain that this process of water loss is called *transpiration* in plants.

Suggestion(s) for extension
Cover the leaves of a small branch on a tree, outdoors on a sunny day, with a plastic bag. Pour the collected water into a measuring cup. Repeat the experiment with the same branch on a very dull day. Is there a difference in the amount of water produced? Why might this be?

Suggestion(s) for support
Help the children find differences and similarities between the leaves by asking questions to prompt observation. Are they all the same shape? Are they all the same colour/size? Do they all feel the same when you touch them? Point out the leaf veins. Compare two leaves at a time – what differences can be noted in the veins? Show an example of a simple leaf and a compound leaf. Can the children find other examples of these types of leaf?

Display ideas
Make headings such as 'rounded edge', 'jagged edge', 'simple', 'compound', 'small', 'large', 'smooth surface', 'hairy surface' and so on. Mount these on the wall, together with the children's observational drawings of leaves which belong to each category. Place a table underneath the display with the collection of house plants on it, to demonstrate different leaf types.

Other aspects of the Science PoS covered
Experimental and Investigative Science – 1b; 2a, b; 3b, c, d.

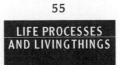

HOW PLANTS MAKE FOOD

Green plants are able to make their own food.

†† *Small groups.*

⏲ *30 minutes initially. 30 minutes after experiment.*

⚠ *Teacher supervision is necessary for the use of chemicals, handling fire and the use of the cooker.*

Previous skills/knowledge needed

Plants are living things. Leaves have a particular function in plants.

Key background information

Green plants are the only living things which can make their own food. This process takes place in the leaves. The plant uses carbon dioxide, water and sunlight with chlorophyll in the leaves to produce sugar and oxygen. This process is called *photosynthesis*. The plant then turns some of the sugar into starch for storage in its cells, and thus testing a leaf for starch shows whether or not photosynthesis has taken place.

Preparation

Find a suitable tree with low branches, such as a hawthorn or beech.

Resources needed

Potted plants, a leafy tree, methylated spirits, iodine, card, paper-clips, water, a small saucepan, a cooker, a glass jar.

What to do

Discuss with the children how a green plant makes its own food. Explain that a substance inside the leaves, called *chlorophyll*, is what makes the leaves green; and that this chemical causes carbon dioxide and water to combine in the presence of sunlight, producing a type of sugar. Talk about the importance of the by-product *oxygen* in this process, and the way that plants and animals help each other by each producing a gas that the other needs. How is the way that plants make their food different from the way animals obtain food? Discuss the fact that some plants, like fungi, do not make their own food and that they actually feed on the nutrients within (or released by) other living things.

Explain to the children that they are going to carry out an experiment to find out about photosynthesis. Cover a leaf on a low branch of a tree outdoors with two pieces of card,

secured by paper-clips. After several sunny days, remove this leaf plus another (uncovered) leaf from the tree.

The teacher can then do the following experiment.

▲ Boil the uncovered leaf for a few seconds and place it in a jar with a solution of 70 per cent methylated spirits and 30 per cent water.

▲ Wash the leaf and then ask the children to add a few drops of iodine. What happens? The black colouring shows the presence of starch. Explain that iodine is used to test for starch and that plants turn some of the sugar they make into starch. What does the result of this test show?

▲ Repeat the test with the covered leaf, removing the card first. What happens this time? What does this tell us?

Try the same experiment with plants which have variegated (partly green, partly white) leaves, such as geraniums. Are the results different? Why? Cover only a portion of a leaf (including both a green area and a white area) on a potted plant and repeat the tests. What happens?

Discuss the results. Why do we need to test a covered and an uncovered leaf? Does this make the test fair? Why is it a good idea to repeat an experiment? Do we always obtain the same results? What is the best way to record what happens? Ask the children to write about how a plant makes its own food.

Suggestion(s) for extension

Test for oxygen production in photosynthesis by using water plants such as *Elodea*. Place small plants in two separate jars and cover the plants with water. Cover each plant with a funnel, then invert a test-tube filled with water over the stem of each funnel. Place one jar in the sunlight and one in the dark, then leave them for several hours. Remove each test-tube carefully by placing your thumb over the mouth of the tube. The teacher can then insert a glowing splint into each tube (do not allow the children to do this). The test-tube from the plant that was kept in the sunlight should cause the splint to ignite.

Suggestion(s) for support

Ask the children to tell you what they learned from the experiment. Discuss any aspects of misunderstanding or concern. Explain why it was important to test both an uncovered and a covered leaf. Talk about how plants and animals differ in their methods of obtaining food. (Plants cannot obtain minerals from photosynthesis. How do they obtain minerals? How do animals obtain minerals?) Act as scribe, if necessary, when a child is recording ideas about how a plant makes food.

Opportunities for IT

Children could use a word processor to write and print labels and other information about photosynthesis for a class display.

Display ideas

Make a large model of a plant and the sun from card. Attach these to a display board. Make arrows and labels showing what a plant uses to make food and add these to the picture. Label the parts of the plant. Mount the children's pieces of writing about photosynthesis around the plant.

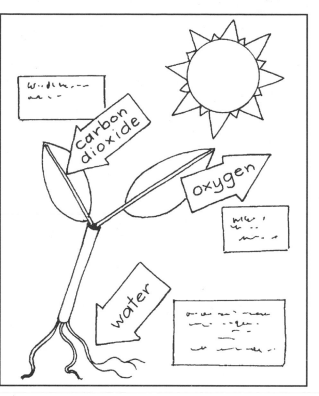

Other aspects of the Science PoS covered

Experimental and Investigative Science – 1a, d; 2a, b, c; 3b, c.

FLOWERS

The flower has a particular function in plants.

†† *Small groups.*

🕐 *45–60 minutes.*

⚠ *Use of the craft knife should be supervised by the teacher. Discourage children from eating flowers or seeds.*

Previous skills/knowledge needed

Plants are living things. Basic facts about the functions of the roots, stems and leaves of plants.

Key background information

Flowering plants have specialised parts adapted for different purposes. The flowers contain the reproductive organs. Most flowers contain both male and female parts. (See Figure 1.)

Flowers are brightly coloured and scented in order to attract insects and some birds. These animals play a vital role in the reproduction of the plants, because they aid pollination.

Pollination must take place before seeds can be produced, and is achieved when the pollen from one flower is transferred to another flower of the same species. Insects collect the pollen on their bodies when they are drinking nectar from the flower, and this pollen can brush or fall off when the insect visits another flower. Wind is another means of pollination.

When a pollen grain lands on the stigma, it sends a tube down the style into the ovary, where the male (pollen) cell combines with the female cell (ovule), resulting in a fertilised egg. The fertilised egg then grows into a seed. After fertilisation, the sepals, petals and stamens dry up. The petals and stamens fall off because they are no longer needed to attract insects, and the ovary develops into a fruit.

Preparation

Obtain a collection of flowers, some of which have a large base or receptacle.

Resources needed

An assortment of flowers, a craft knife, a cutting board, hand-lenses, paper, pencils, a microscope (optional).

What to do

Provide the children with an assortment of flowers and encourage them to look for differences and similarities – colour, shape, size, smell, texture, number of petals, type of stem, number of flowers on each stem, and so on. Each child could make an observational drawing of one of the flowers.

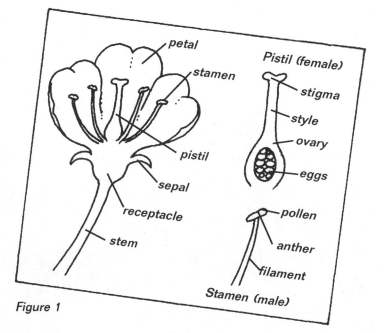

Figure 1

Do the children know why flowers are often coloured and have a scent? Discuss why insects and some birds visit the flowers – what are they after? What happens to a bee when it goes inside a flower? Talk about how pollen is transferred to the bee as it takes nectar from the flower, and how this pollen is transported to another flower. Explain what happens to the pollen once it reaches the other flower, and how seeds are formed. Compare this with human fertilisation, if appropriate. Why do plants need to produce seeds? How can the seeds be dispersed?

Next, cut up the flowers to look at the flower parts mentioned in the discussion on pollination. Using a flower with a large receptacle, carefully cut open the base. The eggs will be visible inside the ovary. Use a microscope, if available, for a more detailed examination. Separate out the pistil, stamen and petals for more detailed observation.

Suggestion(s) for extension

Ask the children to compare two different flowers. How does the size, shape and colour of the whole flower head vary? Do the sizes and shapes of the reproductive organs vary? Are the stamens of some flowers much longer than those of others? Why? The children could also make observational drawings of each separate flower part, labelling each one.

Suggestion(s) for support

Use a plastic model flower or draw the flower parts on card during a discussion about pollination. Ask the children to match the model plant part with the real plant part to assist in identification and naming.

Assessment opportunities

Ask the children to draw and/or write about how flowers are pollinated and how seeds are made. This will enable the teacher to assess how well the individual children have understood the function of flowers.

Display ideas

Make a large picture of a flower using coloured card and pin this on the wall. Label the flower parts. Make three-dimensional models of insects that visit flowers, then suspend these near the flower. Mount the children's observational drawings and writing on card and display these around the flower. Ask the children to write comic strips showing how pollination is carried out and how seeds are formed. Make these into a book or display them alongside the other work.

Other aspects of the Science PoS covered

Experimental and Investigative Science – 2a, b; 3b.

GROWING NEW PLANTS

Plants can be propagated in a variety of ways.
†† *Small groups.*
🕐 *30–45 minutes initially, followed by daily observations of 10 minutes.*
⚠ *Use of the craft knife should be supervised by the teacher.*

Previous knowledge/skills needed

Plants are living things. There is a huge variety of plants. Plants need sunlight, water and nutrients to grow.

Key background information

Most household plants can be propagated quite easily and in a variety of ways. Some of these include: plantlets, which are miniature plants at the ends of flowering stems (as in *Chlorophytum* or spider plant and *Tolmiea* or piggyback plant); offsets, which are miniature plants growing as side shoots from the main stem (as in cacti and Bromeliads); division, where the main plant is divided into two or three (as in *Chlorophytum*, *Maranta* and many ferns); stem cuttings (most house plants); leaf cuttings (such as those from succulents); root cuttings; and seeds.

LIFE PROCESSES
AND LIVING THINGS

Preparation

Obtain some healthy house plants such as *Chlorophytum* (spider plant with plantlets), cacti, succulents, begonias, *Impatiens* (busy Lizzie) and *Saintpaulia* (African Violet), as well as a packet of mixed flower seeds.

Resources needed

Potting compost, plant pots, clear plastic or glass jars, water, paper, pencils, a collection of house plants and seeds (as listed above), hand-lenses, a craft knife, a ruler, a camera (optional).

What to do

Ask the children if they know how new plants can be grown. What methods do they know? Have they grown plants from seed? From cuttings? Discuss the other ways that plants can be grown. Explain that they are going to try out some of these methods, using a collection of house plants. Show them the collection. Do they know the names of the plants? Can they say how new plants could be grown from them? Look at the differences and similarities between the plants. Revise the names and functions of the plant parts and make some observational drawings of them.

Set up the following:

▲ Spider plant – remove a plantlet from the stem and place it in a jar of water.

▲ Cactus – cut an offset from the main stem and place it in a small pot with potting compost and water.

▲ Spider plant – carefully divide a plant into sections with their own roots. Pot with potting compost and water.

▲ African violet – remove a mature leaf from the base of the plant with the stem still attached. Cut across the base of the stem, and plant it in a pot with potting compost and water. The leaf base should be just above the compost.

▲ Succulent – remove a whole leaf and push the end into potting compost. Water.

▲ Busy Lizzie – take a stem cutting, cut off the end and place the cutting in compost. Water.

▲ Seeds – follow the instructions on the packet.

Discuss what the children think will happen. Where will the roots grow from? How quickly do they think the roots will grow? Which new plant do they think will grow best? Why? Talk about the right conditions for plant growth. What will the plants need? When should they be watered?

Once the cuttings and seeds are set up, allow the children time each day to observe what is happening. Take photographs of the plants as they grow. Measure the heights to record any changes. Have the leaves grown or changed in any way? The children could keep a daily diary to record the results and, after several weeks, discuss the outcomes. Which plants grew best? Discuss the reasons for any failures. Are the new plants different from their parent plants in any way? In what ways are they the same? Make observational drawings of the new plants. Repot the plants as they grow.

Suggestion(s) for extension

The new plants could be grown under different conditions to see which condition is best for growing – such as in a warm place, in a cool place, in bright sunlight, in shade, and so on. Comparisons could then be made between the results.

Suggestion(s) for support

Compare just two methods of propagating, to make recording easier; or pair up a child who is good at recording with one who is not.

Assessment opportunities

This activity will enable the teacher to assess the children's recording skills.

Opportunities for IT

Individuals, or groups of children, could use a word processor to write a diary of the plant's growth. This will involve saving and retrieving the diary, and learning ways of formatting and presenting the information.

Display ideas

Put up large paintings or drawings of the plants with labels showing how they can be propagated. Add the children's record keeping and observational drawings to the display, with the actual parent plants on a table nearby. Make books of drawings or photographs of the plants as they grow.

Other aspects of the Science PoS covered

Experimental and Investigative Science – 1b, c; 2a, b, c; 3a, b, c.

SEEDS

Plants disperse their seeds in a variety of ways.
†† *Small groups.*
🕐 *60–120 minutes.*
⚠ *Use of needles should be supervised by the teacher.*

Previous knowledge/skills needed
Plants produce seeds to reproduce themselves.

Key background information
Flowering plants which produce seeds are called *angiosperms*. Non-flowering plants which produce seeds are called *gymnosperms*. All seeds have three main parts: the outer covering or seed coat, the embryo or baby plant and a food store or endosperm. (See Figure 1.)

The food store is the seed's only source of nourishment as it grows underneath the soil. Once the seed grows a shoot above ground, photosynthesis takes over to produce food for the whole plant. Seeds which divide into two parts are called *dicotyledons* (such as beans and peanuts), and seeds which are a single unit are called *monocotyledons* (such as corn and oats).

Seeds can be dispersed in many ways: by wind (ash, dandelion, sycamore); by water (coconut, cranberry, some wattles); by animals (burdock, thistle, berries, nuts); by explosion of a seed pod (sweet peas, violets, broom, gorse). They are dispersed over a wide area for several reasons: to prevent overcrowding near the parent plant; to prevent competition between too many seedlings in one place; and to preserve the seedlings if the parent plant is destroyed.

Preparation
Obtain a variety of seeds of different shapes and sizes. Try to include dandelion, sycamore, thistle, burdock, broom, gorse, elderberry, acorns, conkers, apple pips and a coconut.

Resources needed
A collection of seeds, hand-lenses, paper, pencils, scissors, adhesive tape, adhesive. A variety of materials such as cotton wool, plastic, thin fabrics and thin card plus matchsticks, thread, needles, rice.

What to do
Show the collection of seeds to the children. Do they know the names of the plants from which the seeds come? Ask the children to tell you why plants produce seeds. Do they know how the seeds are dispersed? Discuss the various ways that seeds can be dispersed and choose an example of each type, such as: wind – dandelion; water – coconut; animal – burdock; explosion – broom. Can the children say why the seeds need to be carried away from the parent plant? What might happen if all the seeds landed in the same place?

Study the seeds more closely. What features do they have which are adapted for dispersal? Do the wind-scattered seeds have things in common? Do the seeds which stick to animals' coats look similar in any way? What features would any seeds dispersed by water need? Why? Discuss the size of berries which birds eat. Is this important?

Next, study the dandelion in more detail. Remove single parachutes and provide each child with a hand-lens to look more closely at the parts of the parachute. Then ask them to find out why the parachutes fly so well. Ask some questions to prompt their investigations: Are they all the same size and shape? Do they all drop to the ground in the same way? What happens if you drop them upside-down? What happens if some of the hairs are cut off before you drop the seed? Do wet parachutes fly? Ask them to record their discoveries in

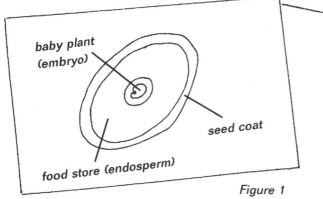

baby plant (embryo)

seed coat

food store (endosperm)

Figure 1

LIFE PROCESSES
AND LIVING THINGS

some way and discuss the findings with the whole group or class. What makes these seeds fly so well? How different are they from aeroplane parachutes?

Challenge the children to make a model parachute of their own which will gently carry a small seed, such as a grain of rice, to the ground. Allow them to decide which materials they will use. Make sure that they record their findings in some way. If they are comparing parachutes within their group, discuss how they can make the test fair. Encourage them to make predictions about the results of any changes they could make to their parachutes.

After each group has tried out its parachutes, bring the whole class together to discuss the results. Drop each parachute to observe how it descends. Which one falls most gently? What helps to slow down the parachutes? This may require some discussion of gravity and air resistance. Does surface area play a part? Is the density of the material important? What difference does the canopy shape make? Does the length of the 'stalk' make a difference?

Suggestion(s) for extension
Make toy parachutes and investigate changing one aspect, such as the shape of the canopy, to see how this alters the parachute's descent. Discuss fair testing, the number of tries and the methods of recording as well as the results.

Suggestion(s) for support
Provide individual children with two identical parachutes and ask them to make observations about how they fall. Challenge them to make one alteration to one of the parachutes and to note the differences in the way it falls when compared with the original. Assist with the recording of the investigation.

Assessment opportunities
This activity will enable the teacher to assess many aspects of Experimental and Investigative Science, such as making predictions, using a fair test, recording, measuring and drawing conclusions. The children could use a record sheet similar to those shown on page 90.

Display ideas
Make a large parachute and suspend it from the ceiling. Attach the children's own parachutes and writing to the large parachute, using cotton thread.

Other aspects of the Science PoS covered
Experimental and Investigative Science – 1a, b, c, d, e; 2a, b, c; 3a, b, c, d, e.

FLOWERING PLANT LIFE CYCLE

Flowering plants have a life cycle.
†† *Whole-class activity, working as individuals or in pairs.*
🕐 *30–45 minutes.*

Previous skills/knowledge needed
Plants are living things. Knowledge of pollination, seed production, seed dispersal and germination.

Key background information
Like all living things, plants have a life cycle. In flowering plants the cycle is: seed, seedling, adult, flower, fertilised egg, seed.

The seeds complete the life cycle of one generation and are the beginning of the next generation.

Preparation
Duplicate the required number of copies of photocopiable page 125 (one per child).

Resources needed
Photocopiable page 125, pencils, scissors, A3 paper, adhesive, reference books on flowering plants.

What to do
Provide each child with a copy of photocopiable page 125. Ask the children to cut out the pictures and place them in what they consider to be the correct order for the life cycle of a flowering plant. How does the plant begin its life – and after that, what stages follow? Ask the children to share their answers with others to see if they agree.

Talk to the class as a whole about each stage. Use their previous experiments and investigations to illustrate points. If appropriate, compare the development of the plant with the stages in the human life cycle.

Next, ask the children to stick the pictures on to a piece of A3 paper so that the pictures form a circle, and draw arrows to show the order of the stages in the cycle. They could then add writing about each stage, based either on reference books or on information gained during previous work on flowering plants.

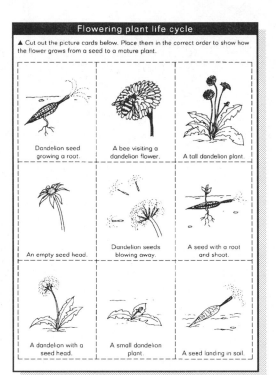

Flowering plant life cycle

▲ Cut out the picture cards below. Place them in the correct order to show how the flower grows from a seed to a mature plant.

Dandelion seed growing a root.	A bee visiting a dandelion flower.	A tall dandelion plant.
An empty seed head.	Dandelion seeds blowing away.	A seed with a root and shoot.
A dandelion with a seed head.	A small dandelion plant.	A seed landing in soil.

Suggestion(s) for extension
Find out about the life cycles of other plants, such as fungi and algae.

Suggestion(s) for support
Help individual children to sort the pictures into the correct order. Talk to the child about each stage. If possible, provide examples of plants in the various growth stages (or use pictures). Match these to the stages shown in the pictures on the photocopiable page. Act as scribe, if necessary, when the child is writing about each stage.

Assessment opportunities
This activity could be used as a means of summative assessment after work has been carried out on flowering plants. The children's written work will reveal their understanding of the stages and processes involved, and will provide a starting-point for the teacher in discussing relevant issues with individuals.

Opportunities for IT
Children might go on to create a multimedia presentation about the plant life cycle. This could include text they have written and pictures taken from CD-ROMs, scanned from their own drawings or scanned from clip art collections. It could even include pictures taken with a school video camera – for example, showing how seeds are dispersed. The presentation could be used as a way of drawing together much of the children's learning over the topic.

If children have not used CD-ROMs or multimedia files before, let them explore a completed file before starting this activity. They need to know how to move around the presentation, how pages are linked and what types of information can be combined in tnis way. A class project can be divided into several smaller parts, with each group taking responsibility for designing and collecting the information for one part of the plant life cycle. Children can start work away from the computer, so that when their turn comes they have already collected and designed the layout of their page.

With first attempts, it is probably best for the teacher to set up the initial structure. The title page will provide the key links to each section of the plant life cycle. This could be a picture of the cycle or a menu (so that clicking on the words 'seed dispersal' takes children to that section of the presentation). Children will then need to be shown how to draw frames, place their data into the frames, add text and edit the page to get the best layout. You might restrict each group to a single page to start with, or allow them a limited number of extra pages. Children will usually need some support for their first attempts, and a timed computer session with parental or other help available is a good idea.

Display ideas
Make a large card flower and staple it to the display board. Make labels to show the names of the parts of the flower. Add information about pollination, seed dispersal and germination. Mount the children's writing and life cycle pictures alongside the display.

Reference to photocopiable sheet
Page 125 could be used again at a later date, to assess retention of knowledge.

Ourselves

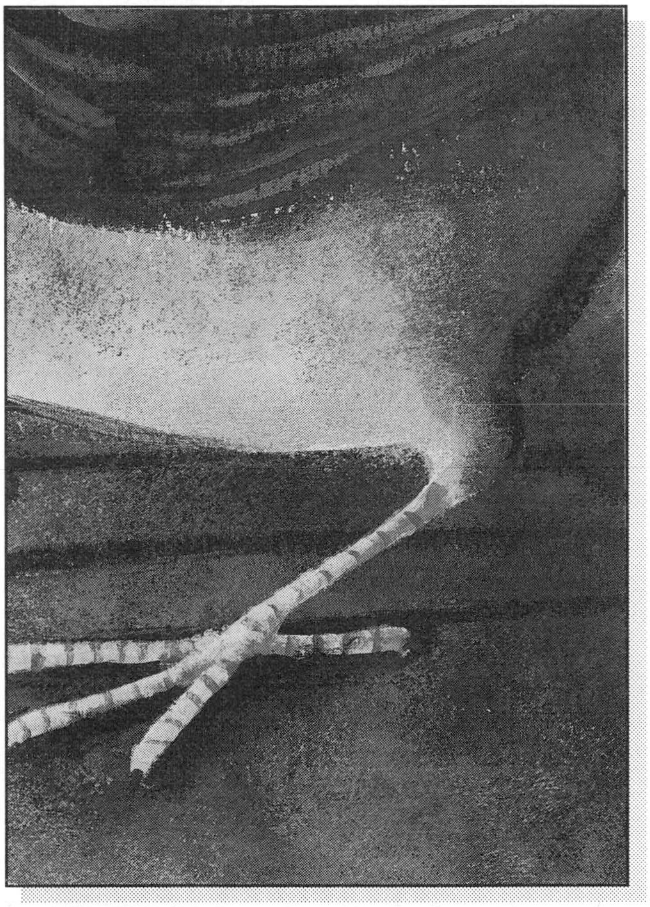

The activities in this section encourage children to explore the similarities and differences between humans, and to take a closer look at the functions of the human body. In the course of carrying out the activities, the children will gain experience in questioning, observing, predicting, recording, measuring and drawing conclusions. They will also have opportunities to work co-operatively and to share their ideas with others.

The activities will look at the human life cycle, as well as exploring the ways in which humans can stay healthy by eating a varied diet and avoiding substances which could be harmful to the body. The children will have an opportunity to examine some of the body parts and functions in more detail, such as the teeth, skeleton, muscles and heart, and to see how these things help us to survive.

LIFE PROCESSES
AND LIVING THINGS

MY FAMILY

There are similarities between humans.

🕇🕇 *Small groups or the whole class.*

🕓 *45 minutes.*

Previous skills/knowledge needed
None specifically required for this activity.

Key background information
All humans have characteristics in common which distinguish them from other animals. Humans are mammals – that is, they give birth to live young, feed their young on milk, are warm-blooded and have hair. But humans have many other features which set them apart from other mammals: they have a larger brain, they walk in an upright position, they are omnivorous, they have a highly-developed spoken language and a very complex social structure. Humans from one family often have very similar features. Hair, skin and eye colouring, shape of hands and size of body can all be inherited.

Preparation
Ask the children to bring in photographs of people in their families, especially parents, siblings, aunts, uncles and cousins.

Resources needed
Family photographs, photocopiable page 126 or 127, pencils, scissors, adhesive, paper, pictures of families from different ethnic backgrounds and places in the world.

What to do
Show the children some pictures of families from other places in the world. What can the children tell about these families by looking at the pictures? Where might they live? What kind of work might they do? What foods might they eat? How can you tell they are all from one family? What features do members of one family have in common with each other?

Talk about humans in general. What things do we all have that make us different from other animals? Discuss how we move, what limbs we have, how we feed, how we breathe, how we communicate, how we live in groups. If appropriate, talk about the features particular to mammals, and mention that humans are mammals too. Divide the children into pairs and ask them to make a list of things humans have in common. Perhaps they can imagine they are writing a list for an alien who has landed on Earth and needs to know how to tell humans apart from other animals. Discuss these lists in groups or with the whole class. Does everyone agree? A large list could be written up for everyone to see.

Next, ask the children to complete as much of photocopiable page 126 as they can at school and then take it home to finish. Explain, if necessary, what each feature on the sheet describes, and use children in the class to demonstrate each feature. When everyone has completed the sheet, bring the class together again to discuss the things the members of each family have in common. This may need sensitive handling, so small-group or even individual discussions may be necessary.

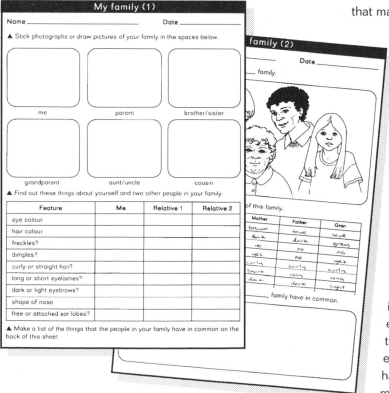

LIFE PROCESSES AND LIVING THINGS

Suggestion(s) for extension

Make graphs of the whole-class results for particular features – for example, graphs of hair and eye colour. Which colours are the most common? Which are the least common?

Suggestion(s) for support

Use the support photocopiable sheet (My family (2), page 127) for those children who would rather find out about a family which is not their own. Act as scribe if necessary, or ask the children to work in pairs to discuss and complete the sheet together.

Assessment opportunities

As the children are writing their lists of things humans have in common, discuss with them the reasons behind their choices. How have they arrived at their decisions? Where have they learned about these things? From observation? Books? Television? Also discuss how humans are different from other animals, perhaps using the children's pets as examples.

Opportunities for IT

The children could use graphing software to create graphs of the different features (eye or hair colour), to interpret the graphs and to ask/answer questions about the information.

Display ideas

Draw pictures and write labels to show the things all humans have in common with each other. Mount these on the wall around a large picture of a human. If the children want to, they could also mount their information sheets about their families and display these next to the other work.

Other aspects of the Science PoS covered

Experimental and Investigative Science – 2b, 3b.

Reference to photocopiable sheets

Photocopiable page 126 is intended for the majority of children to use. Photocopiable page 127 has been included to use with those children who may feel more comfortable finding out about a family other than their own; or alternatively, it could be used as a starting-point for a whole-class discussion.

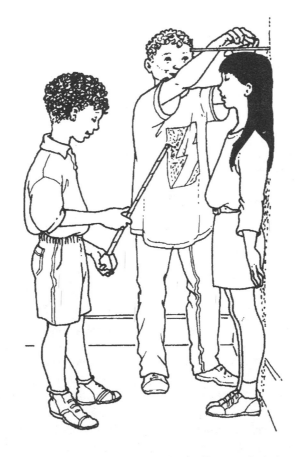

MY FRIENDS

There are differences between humans.

†† *Small groups.*

🕐 *45–60 minutes.*

Previous skills/knowledge needed

Humans are animals. There are similarities between humans.

Key background information

Although humans have many features and characteristics in common, each person is unique and has traits and abilities different from those of others.

Preparation

Duplicate the required number of copies of photocopiable page 128 (one for each child).

Resources needed

Photocopiable page 128, pencils, a stop-watch or watch with a second hand, hand mirrors, a tape measure, bathroom scales, a trundle wheel, pictures of groups of people, chalk, a large open space such as a playground or hall.

What to do

Show the children the pictures of groups of people. Ask them to tell you all the differences they can find between the people in the pictures – height, body shape, hair colour, hair type, eye colour, skin colour, male/female, facial hair, chin shape, freckles and so on. Explain that although humans are very similar, there are also many differences between individuals. Can the children suggest ways in which they are different from people in their family or from their friends?

Explain that they are going to investigate some of their own characteristics and those of others in their group. Distribute copies (one per child) of photocopiable page 128 and explain how to complete the sheet. Ensure that the children know how to use a stop-watch, and how to use the trundle wheel to measure out 25 metres. They will need to mark the beginning and end of the 25 metres with some chalk. Demonstrate how to measure height and weight correctly. The whole class could work

LIFE PROCESSES AND LIVING THINGS

through the activity at the same time, or each group could be allocated its own day of the week to complete the task.

When every group has finished, bring all of the children together to discuss the results. Are there differences in results for each feature between groups? Can the children suggest why this might be? For example, why are some children taller than others? Why can some children run faster than others? Explain that some things can be inherited from our parents and that some things, such as running, can be influenced by past experience and lifestyle.

The children could make bar or line graphs to show the results of the whole class.

Suggestion(s) for extension

Find out about different ethnic groups around the world – what they look like, what they eat and how they live. Compare the features of these people with those of people in our own society.

Suggestion(s) for support

Help with timing and measuring if necessary. Check that the children have recorded their answers correctly. Act as scribe if necessary. Some children could work in pairs rather than in a group, so that they are comparing less information.

Assessment opportunities

This activity will enable the teacher to assess how accurately the children are able to use the measuring apparatus and how well they can present their findings in a graph.

Opportunities for IT

The data collected by the children could be entered into a computer database which they have created in advance. This would make a good-sized database, which children could sort and interrogate to look for links between people's features.

It can take some time to create a class database on the computer, and this activity needs to be spread out over several weeks. Start the process off with a lesson which introduces the data collection; then follow this with another short session on using the computer, so that the children know how to enter, edit, save and retrieve their information. Depending on how much access you have to computers, allow enough time for all the children to enter their data. Make sure that there is plenty of time for the children to use the database they have created before the topic ends.

Before starting to collect the data, it is important to look at the consistency of the data to be collected. Heights need to be measured in the same units throughout, and some agreement about the range of colours of eyes or hair is needed if the database is to be useful later on. You may need to restrict hair colours to a prescribed range, so that all children use the same term for blond(e) hair! Some software allows you to design the collection sheet on the screen, which can then be printed out and given to children. As they then enter their data on to the same screen, the database is created for them.

If children work in threes to enter the data, one child can be changed each time and the newcomer can watch and assist the other children as they enter the information. The next change lets the second child enter their data, while the new child watches and supports the process. This provides some continuity and may reduce the support required by the teacher. It is often helpful for one of the children to read out the data to be entered, so that the child inputting the data can concentrate on the keyboard. Other observers can then check for accuracy in such features as spellings and capital letters. Children may need to search the database before entering information, to make sure that the same person's details have not been entered already.

Once the database has been completed, another class session can take the children through the process of sorting and searching the information. Start with simple questions, such as: 'How many people in the class have blue eyes?' This can be extended to 'have blue eyes and fair hair?' For more able children open-ended questions, such as 'Do tall people have large feet?', can provide a starting-point for learning how to phrase their own questions. Sorting by height and displaying the results will tell the children who is the tallest person in the database.

Children can then work in small groups to answer some prepared questions, follow their own lines of enquiry and make up some questions for other children to answer. They can also be introduced to the graphing facilities on databases which they can use to present their results in a pictorial style.

Encourage the children to look at the accuracy of the answers. If they are working with information on children they know they may be surprised when certain answers do not appear correct. If this happens, encourage children to check the question asked, or the individual records. If mistakes are found, they should edit the data. Such errors can also be used to focus on discussions about the need for accuracy, and how mistakes can occur. Computers rarely make mistakes, but people do!

My friends

Name _____ Date _____

▲ How different are you from your friends? Complete this page to find out.

Feature	Me	(Name)	(Name)	(Name)	(Name)
height (cm)					
weight (kg)					
eye colour					
hair colour					
freckles?					
arm length (shoulder to end of 3rd finger)					
distance around wrist					
shoe size					
shortest time to run 25 metres					

Now answer these questions:

Who is the tallest? _____

What is the difference (in cm) between the shortest and the tallest person?

_____

Does everyone in the group have freckles? _____

Who has the shortest arm length? _____

Does the tallest person have the longest arm length? _____

Does the shortest person have the smallest shoe size? _____

Who can run 25 metres in the shortest time? _____

Display ideas

Make a display of the bar or line graphs showing the class results. Write some questions on card to place around the display, to encourage the children to read and interpret the graphs. Add some photographs or self-portraits of the children themselves, with a heading such as 'We are all different' or 'We are all unique'.

Other aspects of the Science PoS covered

Experimental and Investigative Science – 2a, b, c; 3a, b, c.

Reference to photocopiable sheet

The children will need to fill in information about themselves, as well as about the people in their group.

CHANGES

Humans grow and change.

†† *Pairs or small groups.*

🕐 *30 minutes initially. 10–20 minutes once a month.*

Previous skills/knowledge needed

There are differences and similarities between humans.

Key background information

Children of the same age will invariably be of different heights and weights. This is due to a combination of hereditary factors and environmental ones (such as diet) which influence the rate of growth.

Preparation

Duplicate the required number of copies of photocopiable page 129 (one per child). Ask the children to bring in photographs of themselves at different ages.

Resources needed

Photographs of the children, photocopiable page 129, pencils, a height measurer or measuring tape, bathroom scales.

What to do

Arrange the children into pairs or small groups and ask them to share their photographs with each other. Can they see ways in which they have changed since the photographs were taken? Look at facial and body shape, hair colour and length, height, and so on. Discuss with the whole group or class the features which change as we get older. When do we stop changing? Are we changing all the time? Discuss the stages in the human life cycle, from babyhood through to old age. What are the main changes that take place during each stage? Can the children suggest why some of these changes occur? For example: Why do older people lose height? Why do older people have wrinkly skin? How do babies learn to talk/walk?

Next, provide each child with a copy of photocopiable page 129 and explain that they are going to find out how much their bodies grow and change over several months. Discuss how the sheet should be completed. Demonstrate how to measure height, weight and body dimensions accurately.

Changes in me

Name _____   Date _____

▲ How much will you grow over several months? Carry out these measurements to find out.

date	height (cm)	weight (kg)	length of foot from toe to heel (cm)	waist (cm)	wrist (cm)	length of hand 3rd fingertip to wrist (cm)	neck (cm)

▲ Use this graph to record the changes in your height.

Height in cm

Month

After the children have made their starting measurements, ask them to predict what changes will take place after one month. Which things might change? Which things will not change? Can they give their reasons for thinking this? Discuss others in the class also. Do they think the tallest person will still be the tallest in one month/two months? Which part of the body do they think will grow the fastest? Why?

Over a period of several months, give the children time to repeat the measurements once each month. Then, after this time has passed, compare the results. Who has grown the most during this time?

What feature has changed the most in most people? Were the children's predictions correct? Are they surprised by the results? Discuss the use of averages, and find out what the average height and weight increase has been for the whole class. The children can draw a bar or line graph showing the results each month for some, or all, of the variables being measured.

Suggestion(s) for extension
Compare the rates of growth shown by the graphs. Which children have grown the fastest – those who were the tallest at the beginning, or those who were the shortest? Does the weight graph show gains at particular times of the year? What reasons could there be for this?

Suggestion(s) for support
Assist individual children in measuring and recording to ensure accuracy. Help with the recording of the graphs. Some children may find it easier to record only some of the measurements, for example height, weight and length of foot.

Assessment opportunities
This activity will enable the teacher to assess how accurately the children can use measuring instruments, and how well they can record their results in tables and graphs.

Opportunities for IT
Children could record their personal information in a tabular form using a spreadsheet. Each column could be for a different measurement and each row for a different date. Using simple formulae, children could calculate such things as the changes in height over the recording period. Line or block graphs could be drawn of the most interesting measurements, and patterns could be examined by creating scattergrams. Interesting information could be transferred

on to a class spreadsheet with different names for each column and dates for each row. Comparisons could then be made for different people.

Display ideas
Display the children's photographs of themselves. Write labels which ask questions about the changes that have taken place in the photographs. Make a large table of the children's records at the beginning of the investigation and at the end. Write questions about this to encourage the children to discuss the changes that have taken place.

Other aspects of the Science PoS covered
Experimental and Investigative Science – 1a, b; 2a, b, c; 3a, b, c, d.

Reference to photocopiable sheet
It may be best for the teacher to keep all of the children's sheets in one folder, so that they do not get lost! The activity will provide the children with experience of recording on tables and graphs. When using the graph on the photocopiable sheet, the child can start the height axis with the first recorded measurement and then go up in 0.5cm, 1cm or 2cm increments, whichever is most appropriate.

FOOD
Humans need food and water for activity and growth.
†† *Whole class.*
🕐 *30 minutes initially. 5–10 minutes, three times a day, for one week.*

Previous skills/knowledge needed
None specifically required for this activity.

Key background information
All living organisms need food to provide energy and raw materials for growth, repair and movement. Food eaten (by animals) is converted by digestion into simpler substances, which are used by the cells in the body. Water is essential for the various chemical changes which occur in the body.

Preparation
Prepare a completed example of a child's 'food diary' for one day on a large piece of paper. Figure 1 shows one possible format for a weekly food diary.

Resources needed
Pencils, a large copy of a food diary.

What to do
Show the children the copy of a food diary for a child for one day. Ask them to compare this list to the foods they eat. Do they eat more or less in each meal than the diary writer? Would they drink more or less than this person in one day? Are their favourite foods included here? Do they dislike any of these foods?

Ask the children to tell you why we need to eat and drink. What is the food we eat used for? How do our bodies use it? How long do the children think they could survive without food/water? Discuss the meaning of 'fasting', and how the word *breakfast* is used to describe how the nightly fast is broken by the morning meal. Do the children have the same foods each week? Why? What are their favourite snacks? Who decides what they eat? What do babies eat? Why is this different from the food older children eat? Do adults eat more than children? Why?

Next, hand out copies of your 'food diary for a week' template or help the children to devise their own, and explain that they are going to keep a record of all the food and drinks they consume in one school week. Demonstrate how to fill in the diary correctly by using the first day's meals. Agree on a way to describe the amounts consumed, for example spoonfuls, servings, cups, and so on. Help the children to complete the diary for that day. Then allow them time each day to fill in their food diary – perhaps after register call to record the evening meal, supper and breakfast; after break (and perhaps at other times) to record snack foods; and after lunch to record the midday meal.

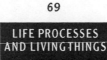

My food diary

Name _____ Date _____

▲ Use this sheet to help you complete your food diary.

Breakfast

| cereal | toast | milk | tea | orange juice |

Snacks

| chocolate | crisps | fruit | cake | biscuits |

Lunch

| chips | meat/fish | sandwiches | yoghurt | fruit juice |

Evening meal

| vegetables | meat | potatoes/rice | fish | ice-cream | hot drink |

After one week, discuss the results. Divide the children into pairs, so that they can share their diaries with each other. Then bring the whole class together again. Were the children surprised by the amount of food they consumed? Do some children eat more than others? What could be the reason for this? (Be sensitive in dealing with children who have weight problems, eating disorders or dietary restrictions. Be aware of possible wealth/poverty issues as well.) Do children who play a lot of sport eat more? What foods seem to be the children's favourites? What foods are not eaten very often? What drinks are the most popular? Some of these questions could be answered by keeping a tally of particular foods eaten over the week.

Suggestion(s) for extension
Ask the children to write a food diary for a younger person or a baby and for an adult in their family. Compare this diary with their own. Who eats the most? Why? Do people of different ages eat different food? Why?

Suggestion(s) for support
Act as scribe if necessary when the children are completing their diaries, or use your own completed food diary as a support sheet. Photocopiable page 130 could be used as a visual and language support sheet.

Opportunities for IT
When the initial collection of data has been made, children could add up the quantities of the different sorts of food eaten and enter their totals into a computer database. This could have been prepared by the teacher beforehand. There will need to be some discussion about which foods to include, and the correct way to measure the quantities. The children can then interrogate the database to look for relationships between different types of food.

Display ideas
Draw large pictures to show all the food consumed in one week by each child, and mount them on the wall. Add the food diaries and provide a collection of books about food nearby.

Other aspects of the Science PoS covered
Experimental and Investigative Science – 2b; 3a, b.

Reference to photocopiable sheet
Page 130 can be used to show the types of food we need.

	Monday	Tuesday	Wednesday	Thursday	Friday
Breakfast					
Break					
Lunch					
Snack					
Evening meal					
Supper					

Figure 1

LIFE PROCESSES AND LIVING THINGS

HEALTHY DIET

A varied diet is needed to stay healthy.

†† *Whole class.*

🕐 *45–60 minutes.*

Previous skills/knowledge needed
Humans need food and water for activity and growth.

Key background information
Good nutrition can be achieved by eating the right kinds of food. Different foods provide us with different substances essential for growth, activity and body repair. *Carbohydrates* provide us with energy and include sugars, starches (cereals, root vegetables) and cellulose (vegetables and grain). (Humans cannot digest cellulose, but many animals can.) *Fats* are more concentrated sources of energy. They are stored in the body as an energy reserve. Fatty tissue helps to support body organs, and stored fats help to protect us against cold. Fats are found in butter, oils, nuts and meat. *Proteins* are necessary for growth and body repair. They are found in meat, fish, eggs, poultry, dairy products, cereals, nuts, beans and root vegetables. *Mineral salts* are needed for growth and health: calcium and phosphorus are needed for bone and tooth development; iron is necessary for the formation of red blood cells; iodine is necessary for the thyroid gland to function correctly. Other minerals such as sodium, potassium, sulphur, copper, manganese, zinc and cobalt are also necessary for body processes. *Vitamins* are also present in food and are essential for growth and health.

A balanced daily diet consists of two or three 'servings' (normal quantities for a meal) of bread, cereal, vegetables, water and fruit; one 'serving' of milk, fish, cheese, pulses, meat/poultry, soya products, eggs and/or nuts; and very small amounts of sugar, oil and margarine/butter. It is normally considered healthy to eat three meals a day, with snacks comprising fruit and low-sugar foods. Fresh foods are preferable to processed foods.

Preparation
Cut out pictures of various foods and stick them to a large sheet of paper in the following food groups: *Group 1* – breads, cereals, vegetables, water and fruit; *Group 2* – milk, fish, cheese, pulses, meat/poultry, soya products, eggs and nuts; *Group 3* – sugar, oil, margarine/butter. Alternatively, obtain examples of real foods to make up each group.

Resources needed
A large chart showing food groups or a selection of real foods, paper, pencils, scissors, colouring pencils.

What to do
Talk to the children about the foods they eat. What do they have for breakfast, lunch, dinner, snacks? Do they vary their diet, or do they eat the same things every week? Who chooses what they eat? What drinks do they have? Write down all the things they eat on a large piece of paper or the chalkboard. Can the children tell you which foods on this list are good for them and which ones are not? Can they say why? Do some foods cause tooth decay? How many of the children have fresh foods daily? How many of the children mainly have processed foods? Can the children suggest which of these is healthier? Why? What problems can overeating cause?

Talk about the various components of food: carbohydrates, proteins, fats, mineral salts and vitamins. Use the food group chart or a collection of real foods to show which foods contain

these substances. Discuss the importance of a varied diet which includes servings from each food group. Discuss what quantity of each type of food is necessary. Talk about some of the diseases that can be caused by vitamin deficiencies – for example, lack of vitamin D (found in fish, oils, butter, egg yolk, liver) causes rickets and soft bones; lack of vitamin C (found in citrus fruit, other fresh fruits and vegetables) causes scurvy (sore mouths and slow healing); lack of Vitamin B (found in pork, liver, whole grains, nuts) causes poor muscle tone, depression and irritability.

Next, ask the children to think about how they can stay healthy by planning what they eat more carefully. Divide the children into pairs and ask them to plan menus for a day, taking into consideration the ideal amounts required from each of the three food groups mentioned. When they have done this, share the ideas of each pair with the whole class. Does everyone agree? Discuss what the children think they may need to change about their current diet in order to eat more healthily. The children could then go on to plan a week's menu which might provide an ideal healthy diet.

Suggestion(s) for extension
Using the initial list of foods eaten by the children, ask them to make a chart of the foods eaten for breakfast, lunch, dinner and snacks. They could then make another chart of 'ideal' healthy foods and compare the two charts.

Suggestion(s) for support
Pair up children who are good writers with those who are less able, or act as scribe if necessary. Help to plan the meals, reminding the children to consider what quantities of food are required from each food group.

Opportunities for IT
After the children have created their 'healthy menu', they could use a word processor, DTP package or art package to design and create a printed version of their 'menu'. The key emphasis could be on the format, text style and use of colour and graphics. Children could start by looking at a range of menus from restaurants to get some ideas for layout.

Display ideas
Using card for menus, the children can write out lists of ideal healthy foods for restaurants. Display the menus on a table, covered with a tablecloth. Use paper plates containing the various foods made out of paper and card, and set these on the table with cutlery.

OUR TEETH

Teeth have particular functions.

†† *Small groups.*

🕐 *30–45 minutes.*

⚠ *Bear in mind any problems caused by food allergies or dietary restrictions.*

Previous skills/knowledge needed
None specifically required for this activity.

Key background information
Humans grow two sets of teeth: temporary 'milk/baby' teeth and a permanent set. The average adult has 32 teeth, 16 in each jaw. Young children have 20 milk teeth. The upper jaw is fixed while the lower jaw is movable. The teeth are arranged according to their function; in an adult there are four tooth types, each adapted for a different job:

Incisors – Bite and cut food. There are four in the centre of each jaw. They are flattened from front to back, and are sharp and chisel-like.

Canines – Hold and tear food. There are two in each jaw and they are sharp and pointed.

Premolars – Grind and crush food. There are four in each jaw and they have ridged cusps on their surfaces.

Molars – Grind and crush food. They are larger than premolars. There are six in each jaw, if they all grow successfully. The four large molars which grow at the hinge end of each jaw are commonly called *wisdom teeth*, because they do not appear until the person has grown to maturity.

The incisors are usually the first teeth to grow in a baby, and the first molars appear when a child is about six years old. Second premolars appear at about 12 years, and wisdom teeth at about 18–25 years.

Preparation
Obtain a model of human jawbones and teeth if possible.

Resources needed
Safety hand-mirrors, paper, pencils, a model of human teeth (optional), an apple, hard toffee.

What to do
Provide each child with a hand-mirror and ask them to draw a picture of their front upper and lower teeth. Talk to them about the shapes of the teeth. How different are they? Why do they think teeth have different shapes? Do the children in each group have similarly-shaped teeth? Ask them to compare their teeth drawings. Can they count the number of teeth they have altogether? How does this compare with others in their group? Do they have any fillings? Where? Are some of their teeth loose or missing? Which ones?

Discuss the names of the teeth and their functions. Use a model of teeth (if you have one) or the children's drawings to point out the different teeth. Talk about the ages at which different teeth grow. Explain that milk teeth are only temporary. Can they find out how many teeth they may eventually have as adults? Compare human teeth with those of animals. Do all animals have teeth? Why do some animals not need them? Relate the shape and number of teeth in different animals to their type of diet.

Next, cut up an apple and give each child a piece. Ask them to bite and chew the apple carefully while watching themselves in the mirror. Which teeth did they use first/second? What else in the mouth helps them to chew? Discuss why they think we need to chew food before we swallow it. Do the same thing with a piece of hard toffee. Do they use different teeth for this? Why? Why do the front teeth have different shapes from the back ones? Does the apple disappear more quickly than the toffee? What implications does this have? (*Safety note:* be aware of food allergies; parental permission may be required before food tasting.)

Finally, ask the children to write down the information they have discovered about their own teeth, including: the total number of teeth they have; the number of incisors, canines, premolars, molars; how many fillings they have; how many loose or lost teeth they have; a description of the shapes and sizes of their teeth; what they like and dislike about their teeth; and how they used their teeth to chew the apple and the toffee.

Suggestion(s) for extension
Make a graph to show the total numbers of each type of tooth the children have. Ask children in another class how many teeth they have. Make a graph of these totals and compare the two results.

Suggestion(s) for support
Draw the shapes of the different types of tooth on to card and cut them out. Write the names of the teeth below the pictures. Let the children use these cards to compare with their own teeth and to help them remember the names. Ask questions to prompt them to study their own teeth. Are some teeth more pointy? Which ones? Are some rounded? Which ones? Are some teeth larger than others? Are some teeth flat? Why do you think this is? Why do you think the sharp teeth are at the front?

Opportunities for IT
A computer graphing package could be used to draw graphs of the number of teeth for a range of pupils. If a spreadsheet is used and the children are represented by numbers rather than names, several sets of data could be included on the same spreadsheet. The tooth count from children in older or younger classes could be compared and graphs drawn to show the differences.

Alternatively, children could enter the information into a database which simply shows name, age, sex, and total number of teeth. Other fields could be included after discussion by the children. Data could be collected across the whole school and at home. The database could then be interrogated to find out whether all seven-year-old pupils have the same number of teeth; or the children could sort the data by age to show numbers of teeth, and so on.

Display ideas
Make a large two-dimensional card model of human teeth. Label it with the names and functions of the different types of teeth. Mount these on the wall, together with the children's writing about their own teeth. Add pictures of other animals' teeth. Add question cards which encourage the children to compare human teeth with those of other animals.

Other aspects of the Science PoS covered
Experimental and Investigative Science – 2a, b; 3b.

DENTAL CARE
Teeth need special care.
✝✝ *Small groups.*
🕐 *30–45 minutes.*
⚠ *Toothbrushes should not be shared.*

Previous skills/knowledge needed
Humans have teeth and these teeth are specially adapted for different purposes.

Key background information
All types of human teeth have three parts:
The crown – the part which is exposed above the gum.
The neck – the part just below the gum.
The root – the part which anchors the tooth in the jawbone.

Inside the tooth there is a *pulp cavity*, filled with blood vessels and nerves, which receives nourishment for the whole tooth. *Dentine* surrounds the pulp, and the dentine in the crown is covered by a hard surface called *enamel*.

Enamel is very strong, but tooth decay can be caused by acids formed in the mouth from sugars and starches which remain between the teeth after food is eaten. The acids form 5 to 20 minutes after eating, and so it is essential to clean the teeth by brushing or rinsing with water after eating. Saliva helps to prevent tooth decay by neutralising the acids.

Dental decay can be prevented by only eating sugary food at mealtimes, not as snacks; by brushing teeth and rinsing after eating; by using a fluoride toothpaste; by eating a well-balanced diet; and by visiting the dentist regularly.

Preparation
Obtain some dental disclosing tablets and a toothbrush, an illustration showing parts of the tooth, a drawing of a tooth on a large piece of paper and a model of human teeth.

Resources needed
Dental disclosing tablets, safety hand-mirrors, a toothbrush, a model of human teeth (optional), paper, pencils, an illustration showing tooth parts, dental floss, the children's own toothbrushes and toothpaste.

What to do
Explain to the children that they are going to learn how to care for their teeth. Revise the names and functions of the teeth, then use the hand-mirrors to locate the different types of teeth. Show the children the illustration of the parts of a tooth, and discuss the role each part plays.

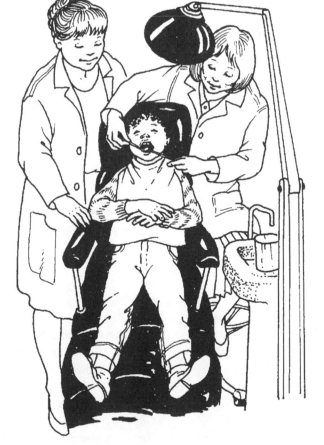

Ask the children whether they have ever had a cavity in their teeth. Do they know why it happened? Talk about how acids are formed in the mouth after eating sugary foods, and how these acids can eat away at the teeth. Can the children tell you how they think they could prevent the acids from causing decay? Discuss the types of drinks the children consume. What could they drink instead of sugary drinks? What foods should they eat to help avoid tooth decay?

Use a model of human teeth, if possible, and a toothbrush to discuss how to brush teeth correctly. Explain that it is important to brush the gums as well as the teeth, and that the children should brush across the gums, down from the gums and between the teeth. Show them some dental floss. Do they know what it is used for? Discuss how to use it correctly. Ask the children to chew a dental disclosing tablet to show where plaque gathers. Are the results different for different people? What does this tell us about how we should clean our teeth? The children may need to use their own toothbrushes and toothpaste to clean the colouring from their teeth. (*Safety note:* toothbrushes should not be shared.)

Ask the children how often they visit the dentist. Can the group agree on what the ideal number of visits in one year would be? Why is it important to go to the dentist? How can this help to prevent tooth decay? Why is it important to protect our teeth? Are false teeth as good as our own? Ask a dentist to visit the school to talk about dental care, or take the children to visit a dental surgery.

Suggestion(s) for extension
Ask the children to draw and/or write step-by-step instructions on how to clean teeth correctly.

Suggestion(s) for support
Some children are very sensitive about the appearance of their teeth, so the teacher will need to be aware of this. Discuss the fact that people differ from each other in many ways, and that teeth are just one aspect of this.

Assessment opportunities
Ask the children to write a list of ways to look after our teeth and ways of preventing tooth decay. The list will enable the teacher to assess how much of the information has been understood by individual children, and will also provide a good starting-point for further discussion.

Opportunities for IT
Children could use art or drawing software to create posters about dental care, or write rules for 'how to look after your teeth' which could be included in a dental care display.

Display ideas
Use the lists the children have compiled to make posters about dental care. Display these near the school toilets and the canteen. Make a large picture of a toothbrush. Mount this on the wall and pin information labels about how to care for teeth around it.

Other aspects of the Science PoS covered
Experimental and Investigative Science – 2a, b.

OUR SKELETON

The skeleton provides support for the body.

†† *Pairs.*

🕐 *45–60 minutes.*

Previous skills/knowledge needed
How to use a measuring tape correctly.

Key background information
The human skeleton is made up of 206 bones. The skeleton has two main functions: to protect and support the internal organs and to provide attachment for the muscles which are used for body movement. Most bones have a common name and a medical name – skull/cranium, jaw/mandible, collarbone/clavicle, shoulder-blade/scapula, upper arm/humerus, breastbone/sternum, rib/rib, backbone/spinal column, lower arm-bones/radius and ulna, wrist-bones/carpals, bones of the hand/metacarpals and phalanges, thigh-bone/femur, kneecap/patella, lower leg-bones/fibula and tibia, ankle/tarsals, bones of the foot/metatarsals and phalanges.

Preparation
Duplicate the required number of copies of photocopiable page 131 (one per child).

Resources needed
Photocopiable page 131, pencils, a measuring tape, reference books on the human skeleton.

What to do
Hand out copies of the photocopiable page to the whole class. Explain to the children that they are going to find out about the human skeleton, and that the drawing on the sheet shows the bones in the human body. Go through the names of all the bones on the sheet and ask the children to find these bones in their own bodies. Can they count the number of bones in the fingers of their hand? (14.) Which is the longest bone in the hand? Which bones look the most fragile? Why do the hands and feet need so many bones? Which bones in the body have to move the most? Why do the children think the breast-bone is wide and flat? Look at the shapes of the bones at the top end of the upper arm and leg. Explain how a ball and socket joint works, and how this helps movement. Draw a diagram if necessary.

Talk to the children about the bones in our bodies. Why do we need a skeleton? What does it do? Do other animals have them? Can they name any animals which do not? Why do these animals not need a skeleton? Ask if anyone has broken a bone. What happened? How was it mended? What might have happened if the break was not properly corrected?

Next, ask them to work in pairs to measure the bones in their bodies and fill in the record sheet. Explain how to use the measuring tape correctly, and how to complete the record sheet. When they have done this, compare the results. Are the bones of different children different in length? Do the tallest people have the longest bones in their arms and legs, or just in their legs? To what extent do the circumference of the head, wrist and ankle vary? Do people of the same height have bones of the same length?

Finally, ask the children to tell you if they know any of the medical names for bones. Allow them time to use reference books to find out the medical names of any other bones. These names can be added to the worksheet.

Suggestion(s) for extension
Make graphs to show the different lengths of the bones of the children in the class. Compare the children's heights with the lengths of their thigh bones. Do the tallest people have the longest bones?

Suggestion(s) for support
Assist those children who need help with measuring and recording, or delete some measurements from the sheet before photocopying in order to reduce the amount of measuring required of some children. Ask questions as the children are measuring to prompt them to think about their bones. Which bones can you move easily? Why do they need to move? Which bone is the longest? Which one is the shortest? Is your hand the same size as your friend's? And so on.

Assessment opportunities
This activity will enable the teacher to assess how accurately the children can measure and record their results.

Opportunities for IT
Children could record their measurements in tabular format using a spreadsheet. They could use the spreadsheet to work out average lengths of bones, average for boys/girls, and so on. More able pupils could explore ratios (such as that of height to thigh-bone length) to see if there is a constant. The spreadsheet can be set up to calculate the ratios automatically, and the answers can be displayed. Different pupils could investigate other ratios.

My bones

Name _____ Date _____

▲ Work with a partner to measure these bones in your body, using a measuring tape. Fill in your answers on the right of this sheet.

Labels: skull, jaw, collar-bone, shoulder-blade, upper arm, breastbone, rib, backbone, hip bone, lower arm, wrist, finger-bones, thigh, kneecap, lower leg, ankle, foot-bones

Measurements:
- distance around head ___ cm
- distance from base of neck to top of arm ___ cm
- length of second finger ___ cm
- distance around wrist ___ cm
- length of lower arm from elbow to wrist ___ cm
- length of upper arm from shoulder to elbow ___ cm
- length of thigh from hip to knee ___ cm
- length of lower leg from knee to ankle ___ cm
- distance around ankle ___ cm
- length of foot from heel to tip of big toe ___ cm

Display ideas

Make a large outline drawing of the human skeleton. Label the bones with their names. Mount this on the wall, together with any graphs the children have drawn. Display books and models of bones on a table near the wall display.

Other aspects of the Science PoS covered

Experimental and Investigative Science – 2a, b, c; 3a, b.

Reference to photocopiable sheet

Pair up able readers with less able ones if necessary to complete the activity.

OUR JOINTS

Joints allow movement of our bodies and limbs.
†† *Whole class or small groups.*
🕐 *45–60 minutes.*
⚠ *Teacher supervision will be necessary when using the craft knife.*

Previous skills/knowledge needed

The skeleton provides support for the body and enables it to move.

Key background information

A joint is a place where one bone joins another. It may be immovable (as in the joints in the skull of an adult) or movable. There are three main kinds of movable joints:
Ball and socket joints – as in the bones of the upper arm and shoulder, or the upper leg and hip. This joint allows the widest range of movement.
Hinge joint – as in the jaw, elbow, knee and fingers.
Plane joint – as in the wrist and ankle. These joints are made up of many small bones whose flat surfaces slide over one another.

Bands of tissue called *ligaments* join the bones of movable joints, and a sprain can occur when a sudden movement pulls the ligament and causes it to tear.

Preparation

Duplicate the required number of copies of photocopiable page 132 (one for each child).

Resources needed

Photocopiable page 132, pencils, card, scissors, rubber bands, paper-clips, a craft knife, three pieces of balsa wood (15cm long x 1cm square), balsa wood glue, ping-pong balls, adhesive tape, thin dowelling or pencils, egg-cups.

What to do

Explain to the children that they are going to find out about how our bodies move. Ask them to tell you what parts of the body help us to walk, run and change position. Discuss the human skeleton, and how it maintains our body shape and aids movement.

Discuss the movements of various body parts. How many different ways can we move our head, neck, shoulder, elbow, wrist, whole arm, fingers, hip, leg, knee, ankle and toes? Allow the children to try out different movements to find their answers. (*Safety note:* make sure that the children restrict themselves to gentle, slow movements, so as to avoid injury.) Can we all move in the same ways? Which body part has the most mobility? Which part is the most difficult to move? Which parts do we use when we walk, talk and swim?

Explain that the movement of our bodies is made possible by muscles and joints. Tell the children about the different types of joints and where they can be found in the body. Hand out copies of photocopiable page 132 and ask them to complete the section about naming the joints. Check that their answers are correct. Discuss what kinds of movement the joints allow. Which joint do they think will allow the most movement? Why? Why is a wide range of movement necessary for the upper arm and leg? Why do we use our fingers more than our toes? Discuss what ligaments are and how they aid movement.

Next, ask the children to make models of 'hinge' and 'ball and socket' joints. Figures 1 and 2 provide suggestions for how these can be constructed. Discuss the results. Which type of joint do they think is stronger? Can they suggest

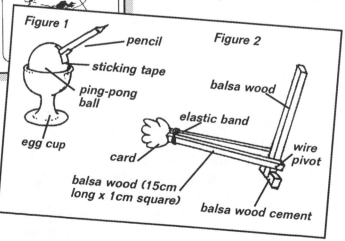

Figure 1
- pencil
- sticking tape
- ping-pong ball
- egg cup

Figure 2
- balsa wood
- elastic band
- card
- wire pivot
- balsa wood (15cm long x 1cm square)
- balsa wood cement

why? Which type of joint allows more movement? (*Safety note*: Teacher supervision will be needed if a craft knife is used.)

Suggestion(s) for extension

Ask the children to make a model skull with a hinged jaw using card and paper-fasteners. Can they make this so that the teeth and jaws are in alignment?

Suggestion(s) for support

Pair up an able reader with a less able reader to complete photocopiable sheet 132. Assist with cutting out and construction if necessary when making the model joints.

Assessment opportunities

Photocopiable page 132 could be used at a later date as a summative assessment activity, to see how much information the children have retained.

Opportunities for IT

Children could use a word processor to write labels or notes for a class display on joints.

Display ideas

Ask the children to draw pictures of all the ways they can move their fingers or other body parts. Mount these pictures on the wall, together with information about the different types of joints in the body. Display the children's models of joints alongside this work.

Other aspects of the Science PoS covered

Experimental and Investigative Science – 2b, 3b.

Reference to photocopiable sheet

This sheet represents three types of joint in the human body: a ball and socket joint (hip), a hinge joint (jaw) and a plane joint (wrist).

MUSCLES

Muscles cause body movement.
†† *Whole class.*
⏱ *45–60 minutes.*

Previous skills/knowledge needed

The body can move and the skeleton and joints aid movement. How to use a measuring tape correctly.

Key background information

The muscles in the human body provide the basic means for all movement. They are attached to the frame of the skeleton, help to give shape to the body, and are found in the walls of some internal organs such as the heart and stomach. They

are attached to bones by strips of tissue called *tendons*. Muscles contract or relax to cause body movement. The skeletal muscles are arranged in pairs, so that one muscle pulls in the opposite direction to another; for example, a *flexor* muscle bends a joint and an *extensor* muscle straightens it out again. Some muscles move involuntarily, such as those of the heart. All muscles are well supplied with blood. The sugars and oxygen carried in the blood give them the energy necessary for work. There are three main types of muscles:
Striated – long muscles, attached to bones.
Smooth – as in the muscles of the digestive tract.
Cardiac – the muscles of the heart.

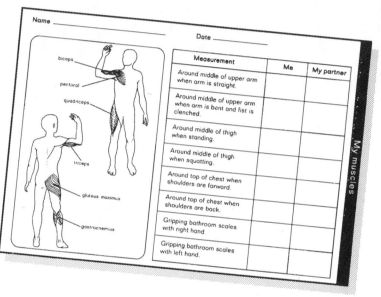

Preparation

Duplicate the required number of copies of photocopiable page 133 (one per child).

Resources needed

Photocopiable page 133, measuring tape, bathroom scales, pencils.

What to do

Explain to the children that they are going to find out about how the muscles in our bodies work. Ask them to tell you what they think our muscles do, and how they help us to move. Explain that muscles are responsible for every movement the body makes (apart from movements caused by gravity); and that as well as those muscles attached to the skeleton, some muscles are found in organs such as the heart and stomach.

Ask the children to look at the muscles in their faces by performing the following actions: open and close nostrils, try to raise and lower ears, open mouth really wide, move mouth up and down, try to pull ears back, raise eyebrows, wink, make the sound 'e', poke tongue out, roll tongue, stretch neck, and so on. Can they find other ways of moving their faces?

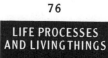

Next, ask the children to feel the muscles in their upper arm by placing one hand on the muscles of the opposite arm while it is by their side and then feeling the muscles move as the bottom part of the arm is raised. Explain that muscles work in pairs and that when they lift their hand, one muscle gets shorter or contracts (the biceps) and the other one relaxes (the triceps). Muscles can only make one movement, and that is to contract. When a muscle is not contracting, it is relaxing. (See Figure 1.)

Ask the children to sit down and cross one leg over the knee of the opposite leg. If they place their hand just below the knee and move their foot, they will be able to feel the leg muscles working. What action do they need to make to feel their thigh muscles (quadriceps) move? In order to feel their calf muscles working, the children can sit down in a chair and place their hands on the muscles of their lower leg. They should then raise and lower their feet on their toes.

Hand out copies of photocopiable sheet 133 and refer the children to the diagrams of the muscles. Can they name the muscles used to make the arm movements? Discuss the three main types of muscle: striated or skeletal muscles, which move the skeleton; smooth muscles, like those of the stomach, which work involuntarily; and cardiac muscles, found in the heart (these also move involuntarily). Talk about voluntary and involuntary movements. Why is it needed for some muscles to move involuntarily? Can we make our skeletal muscles become stronger? How?

Run through the activities on the photocopiable sheet and make sure the children know how to use a measuring tape correctly, and how to grip bathroom scales by resting them on a table and gripping the edge with one hand. Ensure that the children's clothing does not interfere with the measurements.

When they have completed the measuring activities, bring the whole class together again to discuss the findings. Why do the measurements of the arm, leg and chest change? What are the muscles doing? Are the grip measurements for the left and right hand different? Why might this be? Which exercises in physical education would work particular body muscles? Use PE activities to reinforce knowledge about muscle names and functions.

Suggestion(s) for extension
Ask the children to devise ways of investigating the strength of other parts of the body, such as the legs or chest. What exactly will they try to measure?

Suggestion(s) for support
Pair up able readers with less able readers when completing the photocopiable sheet, or act as scribe if necessary. Assist with the measuring if necessary, making sure the children are measuring from zero and not the end of the tape. Make sure the bathroom scales are set to zero before the grip is measured.

Assessment opportunities
This activity will enable the teacher to assess how accurately the children can use measuring tapes.

Opportunities for IT
Children could record the data from their grip tests on a spreadsheet. If the children have the opportunity to make more than one test, the result of each try can be recorded on the spreadsheet and an average result be calculated automatically. The software can be used to plot bar charts for each child's grip.

This activity could be extended to other muscle measurements, with different groups recording different types of measurement.

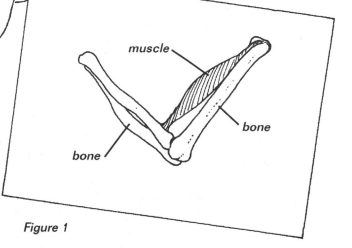

muscle

bone

bone

Figure 1

**LIFE PROCESSES
AND LIVING THINGS**

Display ideas

Draw large pictures of physical education activities which exercise particular body muscles. Label the muscles used.

Add the children's completed activity sheets to the display. Take photographs of the children investigating how their different facial muscles work to produce a range of expressions. Mount and display these alongside the other work.

Other aspects of the Science PoS covered

Experimental and Investigative Science – 1a; 2a, c; 3a, b, c, e.

Reference to photocopiable sheet

If necessary, pair up better readers with less able ones, or read out each task yourself and then ask the children to make the measurement.

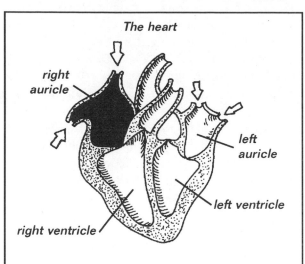

The heart

right auricle

left auricle

left ventricle

right ventricle

OUR HEART

The heart pumps blood throughout the body.

†† *Whole class initially, then pairs.*

🕐 *45–60 minutes.*

⚠ *Teacher supervision is needed when using the craft knife.*

Previous skills/knowledge needed

None specifically required for this activity.

Key background information

The heart is a muscular pump which circulates blood throughout the body. It is situated in the centre of the chest and is roughly triangular in shape. It is divided into four chambers. The two upper chambers, called *auricles*, receive blood from the body and the two lower chambers, or *ventricles*, pump the blood out of the heart. The left side is completely separated from the right side, and there are special valves which allow the blood to flow in one direction only. *Arteries* carry blood away from the heart and *veins* carry it back. Veins can be seen as blue lines under the skin. The blood moves around the body in one direction only. It contains oxygen and food, which are needed by the body's cells and organs in order to function properly.

Preparation

Duplicate the required number of copies of photocopiable page 134 (one per pair of children). Draw or obtain a large diagram of the human heart.

Resources needed

Photocopiable page 134, a diagram of the human heart, a clear rectangular plastic bottle such as an empty cooking oil bottle, adhesive tape, stiff card, scissors, a craft knife, a small heavy weight such as a battery or a marble, pencils, paper.

What to do

Explain to the children that they are going to investigate how the heart works. Can they find their hearts? Ask them to feel their chests to locate the heart. Where is it positioned? Do they know what the heart does? Why does it beat? Explain that the heart acts as a pump to send blood around the body. Discuss why the body needs blood and what the blood contains (oxygen and food). Where does the blood get oxygen from? How does it get food?

Ask the children to look at the blood vessels near the surface of their wrist and lower arm. What do they notice about them? Tell them that the blue blood vessels they can see are called veins, and that veins carry blood back to the heart – whereas the other main type of blood vessel, arteries, carry blood away from the heart. Can they see or feel their pulse? Discuss how the pulse is used as a way of detecting the heartbeat.

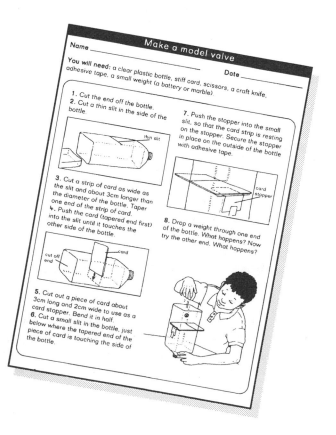

Can the children tell you what shape they think the human heart is? How big might it be? Show them a picture of the heart and tell them that the human heart is about the size of an adult's fist. Talk about the chambers in the heart and what they are called. Explain that there are special valves in the heart and veins which allow the blood to move only in one direction. Refer them to photocopiable page 134, and explain that they are going to make a model of a valve that works in a similar way to those found in the heart. It may be best for some children to make the model during another session, so that only a few children are making the model at one time.

After the whole class have had a go at making the valve, discuss how it works. What problems, if any, did they have making the valve? How did they overcome them? Why is it important for the veins and heart to have one-way valves? Why do the arteries not need them?

Mention that the heart is made of muscle and that as it keeps on beating all our lives, it needs to be healthy and strong. Can the children suggest ways to keep the heart healthy? What things might not be good for our hearts? Discuss the link between smoking and heart disease.

Finally, ask the children to write about and draw pictures of the heart and how it works.

Suggestion(s) for extension
Challenge the children to make a model of the heart and blood vessels using plastic tubing, a plastic hand-pump and plastic valves.

Suggestion(s) for support
Act as scribe if necessary when the children are writing about the heart, or appoint a child as scribe to write down the information for a group of children. Assist with the making of the model if necessary, or prepare a model in advance for the children to use as a guide.

Assessment opportunities
The children's writing can be used as a starting point for discussions about the function of the heart, and may provide some indication of their understanding of the concepts presented in the class discussion.

Opportunities for IT
Children could use CD-ROMs to look up information, and then include aspects of their findings within a drafted account using a word processor. This would involve using the word processor to edit the text taken from a CD-ROM and picking out the most important parts for their account. They could then decide how to present it for the class display.

Display ideas
Draw a large picture of the human heart. Attach information labels explaining how the heart works and what the blood vessels do. Mount the children's writing about the heart on card and add this to the display. Include posters about how we can look after our hearts, and place some of the model valves on a table nearby.

Reference to photocopiable sheet
The model provides the children with a demonstration of how a valve works. It is not intended to be a representation of the heart, but it will serve as a useful discussion point when referring to the way the valves work in a real heart. Make sure there are no sharp edges where the bottle-ends have been cut off. Cover these with tape if necessary.

PULSE RATE

The pulse rate changes with exercise.

†† *Pairs.*

⏱ *45–60 minutes.*

⚠ *Be aware of any child for whom rapid exercise may be dangerous; and be sensitive towards lack of fitness.*

Previous skills/knowledge needed
The heart pumps blood around the body through arteries and veins. How to use a stop-watch.

Key background information
The heart acts as a pump, pushing blood around the body. Each time the heart beats, the beat is called a *heartbeat* or *pulse*. The pulse can most easily be felt in the neck or wrists. Under normal conditions, the heart of an average adult beats about 72–80 times per minute when the body is resting.

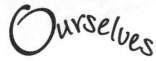

During exercise, however, the pulse rate increases, since the muscles need more oxygen and food in order to work harder. A person's level of fitness can be measured by how quickly the heart rate returns to normal after exercise.

Preparation

Duplicate the required number of copies of photocopiable page 135 (one per child).

Resources needed

Photocopiable page 135, a stop-watch or a watch with a second hand, pencils, paper, rulers, a skipping rope, a large open space.

What to do

Talk to the children about their hearts. What do they do? Why do we need blood to be pumped around our bodies? How can we tell our hearts are beating? Where can we feel the beats? Name the places on the body where the pulse can most easily be felt. It is best to use the tips of several fingers to detect the pulse, as this provides a larger surface to feel the pulse waves.

Explain to the children that they are going to investigate the effects of exercise on their pulse rate. Hand out the photocopiable sheet and run through the procedure with the children. Make sure they can all find their pulse easily and know how to use a stop-watch. Can they predict what will happen before carrying out the task? Can they give reasons for their predictions?

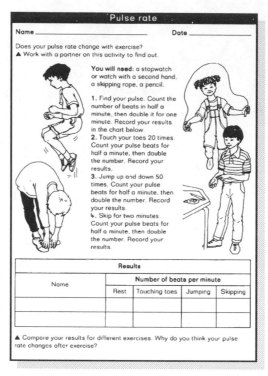

After they have completed the activity sheet, bring the whole class together again to discuss the results. What happened to the pulse rate after exercise? Was this what had been expected? Which activity caused the pulse rate to increase the most? Why do they think this is? Talk about how muscles need oxygen and food in order to work, and how these are supplied by the blood. Are all of the children's results similar? Why might there be differences in results? The children could then write down the conclusions they draw from the activity: why they think the pulse rate changes, and what the body does that causes this.

Finally, the children could draw some bar or line graphs to show the whole class's results for the pulse rate activities. This will give them a clearer picture of the range of pulse rates in the class and how these are affected by exercise.

Suggestion(s) for extension

Repeat the last exercise, skipping for two minutes, and then count the number of heartbeats in half a minute. Then ask the children to sit down and count their heartbeats every two minutes or so, until their pulse rate has returned to the resting rate. How long did it take to return to normal? Why is this different for different people?

Suggestion(s) for support

Some children find it very difficult to find their pulse, so they will need help. Mark the spot with some tape to help them to

LIFE PROCESSES AND LIVING THINGS

find their pulse each time. Pair up able readers with less able ones when completing the activity sheet. Ask questions to help the children consider why the pulse changes. What parts of our body move when we do these exercises? What helps these body parts to move? What do muscles need to work? Why do they need more oxygen and food when they are moving more quickly? The teacher could act as scribe when the children are recording their conclusions, or pair up able writers with less able writers.

Assessment opportunities
This activity will enable the teacher to assess how well the children are able to record their results in tables and graphs. The children's conclusions will be a good starting point for the teacher in assessing what the child has understood.

Opportunities for IT
Children could record their results using a spreadsheet to give a tabular format. They could then work out an average pulse rate for the whole class. If boys and girls are separated they could look for gender differences using averages. Graphs could be drawn from the records made.

Alternatively, children could enter the information into a database. This would enable them to add some other relevant details alongside their pulse measurements, such as their hobbies, weight, height and so on, so that relationships can be investigated – for example, the relationship between the kind of sport being played and the child's pulse rate after the game.

It might be possible to use a pulse measuring device similar to those used on exercise bikes. One such device could be removed from a bike and used by the class to check pulse rates. It is also possible to link a pulse measurer to a computer through an interface, and graphs of pulse rates can be drawn as the children exercise. This gives a pictorial representation of the pulse while the exercise takes place. These graphs can then be printed out.

Display ideas
Draw four large pictures of a child at rest, touching her toes, jumping and skipping. Mount these pictures on the wall and surround each one with the children's graphs of the whole-class results for the corresponding activity. Add the children's pieces of writing about why the heartbeat changes with exercise.

Other aspects of the Science PoS covered
Experimental and Investigative Science – 1a, b; 2a, b; 3a, b, c, d, e.

Reference to photocopiable sheet
Pair up able readers with less able readers if necessary. Make sure the children know what to do, how to use a stop-watch and how to find their pulse easily.

EXERCISE

Exercise keeps our bodies healthy.

†† *Whole class.*

🕐 *30–60 minutes.*

⚠ *Be aware of children who may have fitness problems or may react badly to exercise.*

Previous skills/knowledge needed
None specifically required for this activity.

Key background information
Humans need to exercise to stay healthy. Cardiovascular exercises encourage the heart and lungs to work more efficiently, thereby providing the cells in the body with more effective supplies of food and oxygen.

Preparation
Duplicate the required number of copies of photocopiable page 136 (one per child).

Resources needed
Photocopiable page 136, pencils, reference books on fitness and exercise, paper, pictures of people doing different activities such as reading, gardening, housework, walking, sports, and so on.

What to do
Start off by asking the children what they think exercise is. Show them the pictures of people doing different activities. In each case, ask whether the children think the people are

Exercise

Name _____ Date _____

How much exercise do you and your family do?
▲ Carry out this survey to find out.
▲ Answer the questions yourself, then ask two adults from your family.

Question	(Name)	(Name)	(Name)
How many hours do you sit down at work/school in a day?			
How many hours do you watch TV each day?			
Do you walk to work/school each day?			
Do you walk a dog each day?			
Do you ride a bicycle each day?			
Do you ride a bicycle sometimes?			
Do you play a sport each week?			
Do you do training exercises for a sport each week?			
Do you go swimming each week?			
Do you climb stairs every day?			
Do you go for long walks each week?			
Do you do PE/fitness activities each week?			

▲ Discuss the survey answers with a friend. Do you think you do enough exercise each week?

doing exercise or not. Can they give reasons for their decisions? Why do we need to do exercise? How does it help our bodies? Do animals exercise? How?

Ask the children if they think they do enough exercise to keep themselves fit and healthy. How do they know if they are doing enough? What signs may indicate that we are not exercising enough? Do they think the members of their family exercise enough?

Look at photocopiable page 136 and ask the children to complete the questions about themselves. Compare the answers of the children in the class. Are some doing more exercise than others? Do they feel they get enough opportunities for exercise at school? If not, how could this be improved? How often do they think people should exercise each week? Does this differ for different people? Why? Ask them to take the survey sheet home for two adult members of their family to complete, so that they can discuss adults' responses as well as children's. (*Note:* this may be a sensitive issue for some children, so take this into account.)

Next, provide the children with some reference material on exercise and fitness and ask them to find out about ways of keeping fit. Can they find exercises to strengthen particular parts of the body: exercises for arm strength, leg strength and stomach strength, exercises for the heart, exercises for breathing, and so on? Discuss their findings. Are some activities more suitable for adults than for children? Why? Can too much exercise be harmful? When? How should exercises be carried out? Can exercises cause injuries? How can we find out if we are doing exercises correctly? What happens to our bodies if we don't exercise? After this discussion, the class could agree on a list of suitable activities and exercises for their age group, and this could be incorporated into the class physical education programme.

Discuss the completed survey sheets. Do the children think people in their families are doing enough exercise? Do adults need to exercise more than children? Should all adults do the same types of exercise? How could members of the family help each other to do more exercise? Do we need to do other things as well in order to stay healthy, such as eating the right foods? Collate the class responses and try to compile an agreed list of ways to stay healthy.

Suggestion(s) for extension
Ask the children to make graphs to show the whole class's responses to the survey. This will help them to compare results more easily.

Suggestion(s) for support
Pair up able readers with less able readers when completing the survey. Less able readers could ask their family members to help with the reading of questions at home. Provide positive support for those children who may feel threatened by discussions about their exercise habits. Help them to see the benefits of exercise and discuss any measures which could be taken for improvement.

Opportunities for IT
Children could enter the exercise data they collect into a computer database. They could then look for relationships between exercise and lifestyle. If additional information such as age, occupation and gender are added, other questions can also be asked. The data could also be used to draw graphs of this information. It is also important for children to discuss the accuracy of such information, and the security and use made of data collected about themselves and other people.

Display ideas
Take photographs of the children doing various exercises. Mount these on the wall. Add the children's research about the types of exercises that help particular parts of the body. Make posters showing ways to keep fit.

Other aspects of the Science PoS covered
Experimental and Investigative Science – 3a, b, c.

Reference to photocopiable sheet
Help individual children to read the questions, or pair up better readers with less able readers if necessary. Send home a covering letter explaining the purpose of the survey, if you think this is necessary.

SMOKING

Tobacco can be harmful.

†† *Survey – individual. Discussion – whole class.*

🕐 *Survey – 30 minutes. Discussion – 30 minutes.*

Previous skills/knowledge needed
None specifically required for this activity.

Key background information
Cigarettes contain tobacco. Tobacco smoke contains many chemicals, some of which are known to cause cancer – for example tar, a sticky substance that builds up in the lungs of smokers. Tar prevents the lungs from working correctly, and irritates the lining of the bronchial tubes. Nicotine, another substance found in tobacco smoke, is addictive – which is why smokers usually find it difficult to give up smoking. Nicotine is poisonous. It affects the arteries, making them narrower. This means that the heart has to work harder to pump blood around the body. Carbon monoxide gas is inhaled into the lungs by smokers. It is absorbed into the blood instead of oxygen; but since the body needs oxygen and not carbon monoxide, the smoker must breathe faster to get enough oxygen. Smoking is also a contributor to heart disease, lung cancer, bronchitis and emphysema.

Passive smoking occurs when non-smokers inhale the smoke from other people's cigarettes. Passive smoking can also cause lung and heart disease.

Preparation
Duplicate the required number of copies of photocopiable page 137 (one per child). Explain to the children that they are going to carry out a survey about smoking, and hand out the sheets. Ask them to take the survey home, complete it and bring it back to school.

Resources needed
Photocopiable page 137, pencils, paper.

What to do
After the children have completed the survey, bring the whole class together as a group to discuss the results. Why do they think smokers find it difficult to give up cigarettes? Have smokers noticed any changes in their health which they think are due to smoking? Have most of the smokers tried to give up? Did any of the smokers say they would encourage young people to smoke? Why/why not?

How many of the children's parents smoke tobacco? Do the children like them smoking? (This may be a sensitive issue with some children, so it will need careful handling.) Are they worried about their parents' health? If the parents wanted to give up smoking, how could the children help?

Discuss the answers given by non-smokers. What were the reasons they gave for not smoking? Do they think smoking should be banned in public places? What do the children think? Is it right to ban tobacco smoking altogether? What would smokers think of this? If smoking were banned, what should be done about alcohol, which can also damage your health? What else could be done to discourage people from smoking? Do the children think they will smoke when they are older? Why/why not?

Discuss the effects of smoking: the diseases it causes, as well as the staining of hands and teeth and the odour it creates. Mention tar, nicotine and carbon monoxide and what these can do to your health. Discuss other issues, such as how much it costs to smoke, fire risks, advertising and the viewpoints of tobacco growers and cigarette manufacturers.

Finally, ask the children to design a poster telling people about tobacco smoking and the dangers it causes to health.

Suggestion(s) for extension
Find out about how the lungs work and how important oxygen is to the body.

Suggestion(s) for support
Children who are less able writers and readers could ask the adults to complete the survey for them, or their answers could be recorded on to a tape.

Opportunities for IT
Children could enter the data they have collected into a class database. The data can then be sorted and searched, and

Smoking survey

Name _____   Date _____

▲ Ask two adults (one who smokes tobacco and one who does not) the following questions.

Questions for smoker
How old were you when you started smoking? _____
Why did you start smoking? _____
How many cigarettes do you smoke in a day? _____
Have you tried to give up? _____
What things have you tried to help you give up smoking? _____
Does smoking affect your health? How? _____
Would you encourage young people to smoke? Why/why not? _____

Questions for non-smoker
Did you try smoking when you were younger? _____
Why did you decide not to smoke? _____
Do you think cigarettes should be banned? _____
Should people be allowed to smoke in restaurants? _____
Do you allow smoking in your house? _____
How would you discourage young people from smoking? _____

graphs can be drawn. Some discussion will be necessary to decide the type and format of the data to be collected, to ensure a consistent approach. For such questions as 'Why did you decide not to smoke?', a range of possible answers can be given (including 'None of these') from which people can select an appropriate response. The use of free text fields where comments are made which do not fall into any category might also be explored.

Children should discuss the confidentiality of such information, particularly where names are included, and what use might be made of such a database by tobacco firms, doctors, and so on. Children might also discuss how recorded information can be updated, so that someone who gives up smoking can have their details altered.

Display ideas

Make a large model cigarette from card, showing the ash and smoke. Attach this to a wall and add information labels about tar, nicotine and carbon monoxide and how these affect health. Write a summary of the children's survey to add to the display, and include the children's posters on smoking.

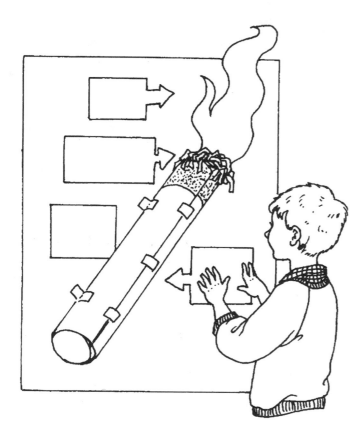

Reference to photocopiable sheet

The children will need to obtain permission to interview another adult if there is no one in their family who smokes tobacco. A covering letter could be sent home to explain the survey before the children take the sheet home. Less able writers and readers could ask the adults to complete the survey for them.

ALCOHOL AND DRUGS

Alcohol and drugs can be harmful.
†† *Whole class initially, then small groups.*
🕐 *30–45 minutes initially. 30 minutes to prepare talk.*

Previous skills/knowledge needed

None specifically required for this activity.

Key background information

Some common drugs include: caffeine (tea, coffee), alcohol, nicotine, morphine, heroin (smack, skag, horse, Henry), cannabis or marijuana (grass, weed, ganja, hemp), cocaine (coke, Charlie, snow, ice, candy, crack), tranquillisers (Valium, Mogadon), barbiturates (barbs, downers, sleeping pills), Ecstasy (MDMA, E), amphetamines (Benzedrine, Dexedrine, uppers, speed) and lysergic acid diethylamide (LSD, acid). All of these drugs can become addictive (addiction can be either physical or emotional). Some drugs, such as tranquillisers, can be prescribed as medicines and should only be used under a doctor's supervision. Many drugs cause illnesses and can cause death.

Medicines such as aspirin, cough mixtures, ear and nose drops, ointments, antacids and antiseptics are safe to use if the correct instructions are followed; but no-one should use another person's medicine, even if they have the same symptoms, because people may be allergic to it or may need a much smaller dosage. Children should not take medicines without adult supervision, and they usually need much lower dosages than adults. Many medicines can have harmful side-effects on our health.

Preparation

Obtain some empty medicine bottles and packets, empty cigarette packets and empty alcohol bottles and cans. Put these on display with a sign asking 'Which of these is it safe to take?' Leave the collection on display for a day. Find out about school policy on where inhalers should be kept, and who is responsible for administering medicines. Is there a designated first-aider? Where are medicines kept at school? Is the school a non-smoking area?

Resources needed

A collection of empty medicine bottles and packets, empty cigarette packets and empty alcohol bottles and cans; paper, pencils.

What to do

Discuss the display of medicines and drugs with the whole class. Ask them to comment on what they think is safe to take. Discuss the amount taken – for example, would it be safe to take a whole bottle of aspirin? Would some of the things make us ill if we took them? What could happen to us? Talk about long-term and short-term effects – for example, smoking over a long time can cause lung cancer, whereas taking a whole bottle of aspirin could cause immediate death. How do children know how much of a medicine to take? Who would they ask or what can they do to find out?

Ask the children to name some medicines they have taken recently. Did they get the medicine from a doctor or pharmacist? Would it be safe for another person to take their medicine? Discuss what might happen if someone took their medicine for the same illness, but was allergic to it. Is it safe for children to take the same medicines as adults? Why not? Can some medicines make you ill? Where are medicines kept in their homes? What other household substances could be dangerous if consumed? What could be done to make sure these substances are kept safely? Are there medicines kept in school? Where? Who should we contact if we need them? Should inhalers be shared? Where should they be kept?

What things would the children describe as drugs? Are cigarettes and alcohol drugs? Why do people take drugs? Discuss the names and types of drugs (see above). What effects can they have on your health? Where can these drugs be obtained? Why is it illegal to sell some of them? Are injections harmful? Discuss injections such as vaccinations and insulin for diabetics, and how helpful these can be. Compare this to the injection of drugs such as heroin. What are the dangers associated with these injections? Why shouldn't you touch syringes found outside? Who should you inform if you see them?

Discuss drinking and smoking. Are these 'acceptable' forms of drug taking? What effects do they have? What harm can they cause? How can smokers affect non-smokers? Is smoking allowed in school? How can drinkers affect non-drinkers (for example, drinking and driving)?

Finally, ask the children to work in small groups to prepare a five-minute talk about alcohol and drugs. The talk should concentrate on safety issues and health considerations, as well as presenting the children's own ideas about whether or not people should take drugs. The talks could be heard over several days.

Suggestion(s) for extension
Ask the children to design posters about alcohol and drugs to represent some of the issues discussed.

Suggestion(s) for support
Help the children to organise their talk. Encourage them to list the good things about drugs and medicines first, and then to list the bad things. Ask them to suggest ways in which medicines can be kept safe, and how children can find out about the dangers of medicines and drugs.

Assessment opportunities
The children's talks should enable the teacher to assess which aspects of the class discussion were understood and taken on board. It will also provide a basis for further discussions with the group or individual children.

Opportunities for IT
Children could work in groups to draft and redraft their talk using a word processor. This could help them to organise and develop their ideas. A final version could be used as part of a display.

Display ideas
Display posters showing the dangers associated with alcohol and drugs. Mount these on the wall behind the collection of empty medicine, alcohol and cigarette containers.

HUMAN LIFE CYCLE

Humans can reproduce.
†† *Whole class.*
🕐 *30–45 minutes.*

Previous skills/knowledge needed
Humans are living things. Knowledge of the life cycles of other animals.

Key background information
Humans need to reproduce in order for the species to continue. Humans are mammals, and like other mammals they give birth to live young. The young are fed on the mother's milk and are cared for by the mother (sometimes with the father's help). Human babies take nine months to develop inside the mother's womb. After birth, the babies take a long time to develop and need a lot of parental care. Young babies cannot walk or talk; these skills are learned over time. Walking babies are called toddlers. Children (in

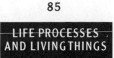

LIFE PROCESSES
AND LIVING THINGS

Britain) go to school at the age of four or five. Teenagers are aged between 13 and 19, and at 18 people (in Britain) are considered to have the legal status of adults. Humans can live to be over 100 years old, but few live to this age.

Preparation
Duplicate the required number of copies of photocopiable page 138 (one per child). Find out about school and LEA policies on Sex Education, to establish the guidelines to be followed when preparing this lesson and when answering any questions which may arise.

Resources needed
Photocopiable page 138, scissors, adhesive, sheets of A3 paper, pencils.

What to do
Talk to the children about the life cycles of different animals. Do they know how frogs develop? What about butterflies? What about mammals such as badgers, or marsupial mammals such as kangaroos? Discuss how the animals are born, how they grow and develop, and how long this process takes. Mention that humans are mammals too, and that we develop over many years from a tiny baby into old age.

Discuss how long it takes for a human baby to develop inside its mother. Talk about the baby at birth. How small would it be? What would it weigh? What can it do by itself? How can the parents help to look after it? What kind of food does it eat? Discuss the various stages of development such as the first appearance of hair, teething (growth of the first teeth), crawling, walking, talking, and so on. Compare this with the development of other animals, and discuss how important it is for adults to care for human babies for a long time before the young humans are capable of looking after themselves.

Discuss growing up and growing old. How can you tell a teenager from a person in their twenties or thirties? What happens to our bodies as we become old? How long do humans usually live for? What problems might people experience in old age? Which stage in life do the children think might be the best? Why? Can they remember what it was like to be younger? What is their earliest memory? How important is it for humans to live in family groups? What advantages does this have? Do other animals live in family groups? Why/Why not?

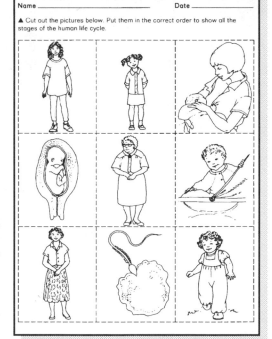

The human life cycle

Name _____ Date _____

▲ Cut out the pictures below. Put them in the correct order to show all the stages of the human life cycle.

Next, hand out copies of photocopiable sheet 138 and ask the children to cut out the pictures and place them in the correct order to show the stages in the human life cycle. Allow them to compare their answers with those of other children. Do they all agree? What clues tell you how old the people are? Provide each child with an A3 piece of paper and ask them to stick the pictures on to the paper in the correct order. Ask them to write some information about each stage in the life cycle. Discuss their writing individually or in small groups.

Suggestion(s) for extension
Find out about the human reproductive organs.

Suggestion(s) for support
Act as scribe, if necessary, when the children are writing about each stage of the human life cycle. Make sure that the stages are in the correct order. Talk about each stage with individual children, and discuss what the people look like and what they are able to do at each stage. Provide a 'question box' for children to write down questions to which they want to know the answers. Assure them that they will get a confidential reply.

Assessment opportunities
While the children are writing about each stage of development, this will be an ideal opportunity to talk to individuals in order to assess their level of understanding about growth and reproduction.

Display ideas
Ask the children to bring in photographs of people in their families at different stages of development: very young baby, baby, toddler, infant, junior age, teenager, twenties, thirties, forties, and so on. Mount some of the pictures on the wall. Ask the children to write about themselves at different ages in their lives, and suggest that they invite parents or grandparents to write about their own lives. Add this writing to the display. Make a display to show other animals and their stages of development.

Reference to photocopiable sheet
If school policy does not allow it, or if you consider the children not to be ready for discussions about fertilisation and development in the womb, cover up these pictures with white paper before photocopying so that the activity can centre on development from birth onwards.

Investigations

Scientific understanding involves both the content of science and the methods by which knowledge is obtained. Experimental and Investigative Science requires that pupils develop the intellectual and practical skills that will allow them to explore and investigate the world of science and develop a fuller understanding of scientific phenomena, the nature of the theories explaining these phenomena, and the procedures of scientific investigation. This should be achieved through activities that require a progressively more systematic and quantified approach, which develops and draws upon an increasing knowledge and understanding of science.

This section contains four activities which provide the pupils with an opportunity to plan and carry out investigations in which they:
▲ ask questions, predict and hypothesise;
▲ observe, measure and manipulate variables;
▲ interpret their results and evaluate scientific evidence.

Within the context of their growing knowledge of life processes and living things, these activities will allow pupils to gain awareness both of the nature of scientific activity and of the basis on which scientific claims are made.

These activities are necessarily more open-ended than those in the other sections of the book; but guidance is given with regard to classroom management, the concepts likely to emerge and how the teacher can use the activities for assessment purposes.

◈ WOODLICE

Can woodlice move on any surface?

†† *Small groups or pairs.*

⏱ *60–120 minutes.*

⚠ *Strict hygiene procedures should be observed in handling soil and woodlice.*

Key background information

Woodlice are small arthropods. There are about 42 different species in Britain. They have a hard outer shell or *exoskeleton* and a soft body with seven pairs of legs underneath. The body is divided into a head, a thorax and an abdomen and has many separate sections or *segments*. Woodlice have two antennae on the head and two pairs of tails (called *uropods*). The uropods help to control water intake. If the body becomes too dry, the uropods are used to suck up water. Woodlice use gills for breathing, which means that they need to live in a damp environment. When they are two years old, woodlice are ready to breed; they can live for up to four years. They mate in the spring and summer. After the female has mated, she moults and the new skin contains a brood pouch (a creamy-white bag between the front legs), into which the female lays up to 200 eggs. The eggs hatch after about 25 days. The young look like small adults, but are white and have six pairs of legs. After the first moult, the young develop seven pairs of legs; they will continue to moult up to ten times before they become adult. In winter, the woodlice burrow into rotting leaves or topsoil to protect themselves from the harsh conditions.

Woodlice can be kept in a waterproof container, such as a fish tank or ice-cream container, in the classroom. Put some soil, fragments of rock, dead leaves and pieces of wood into the bottom of the container and keep the soil damp by spraying a small amount of water on it each day. Woodlice eat fruit or vegetables; they will also benefit from having some cuttlefish bone to keep their exoskeletons hard. Place the container out of the sunlight and away from radiators, and cover the top with some polythene. Pierce a lot of small holes in the polythene covering to allow air in.

Preparation

Prepare a suitable container, as outlined above, and then either collect some woodlice yourself or arrange a walk with the children to collect them.

Allow the children to observe the woodlice over several sessions before starting the investigation. Allow them time to discover such things as: how many legs they have; how many segments their bodies have; how they move; what shapes, colours and sizes they are; what they eat; and so on. Talk to them about careful handling of the woodlice (plastic spoons are useful), and make sure that the children know how to look after them correctly.

Resources needed

Record sheets similar to those shown on page 90 (if needed), live woodlice, a selection of fabrics and materials (such as wool, carpet, smooth plastic, wood, glossy paper, corrugated card, metal lids and cotton wool), hand-lenses, rulers, pencils.

What to do

Explain to the children that they are going to find out how woodlice move and what types of surface they can move on. What things do they think they will need to carry out the investigation? What surfaces would they like to test? Ask them to select the materials from those you have provided; or alternatively, ask them to select their own from those normally available in the classroom. Talk to them about their selection. Are the materials different from each other? Is there a variety of textures/types of surface? How many different surfaces do they think they should test?

Ask them to predict which surfaces the woodlice will be able to walk on. Can they give reasons why? Which surfaces do they think the woodlice will *not* be able to walk on? Why? What things do they think will affect the movement of the woodlice? Would the size of the woodlice have any effect? The length of their legs? The thickness/shape of the material?

Ask them to plan what they are going to do, using record sheets (if needed) similar to those shown on page 90. How do they plan to carry out the investigation? What other things will they need apart from the selection of materials? How will they make sure the test is fair? Which factors will need to

LIFE PROCESSES AND LIVING THINGS

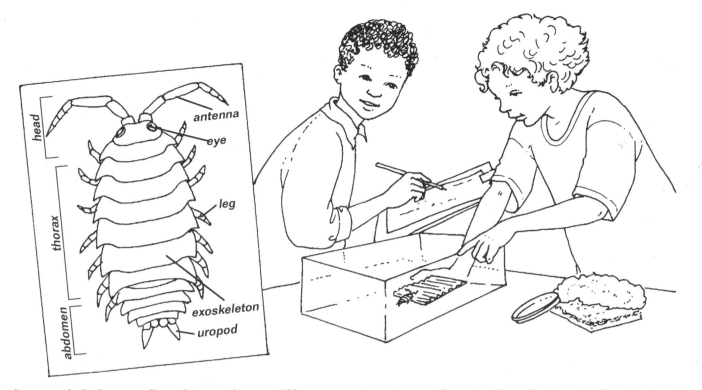

change and which ones will need to stay the same? You may choose to sit with the group as they are planning this, in order to prompt the children's ideas and suggestions and observe how they go about organising the investigation as a group. Help them to plan a 'fair' test if necessary. They should use the same woodlouse each time and place it on each material in the same way. They will need to think about how to decide whether or not the woodlouse has moved on the surface successfully. Does it have to walk a certain distance? Does it have to remain on its feet?

Observe the children as they carry out the investigation. Do they refer to their plan? Are they actually doing what they said they would do, or have changes been made? Who decided on these changes? Are all members of the group participating? How are they recording what happens?

After the investigation, talk to the group about what they have discovered. Were the results expected? Why/why not? What factors influenced the ability of the woodlouse to move on the different surfaces? What problems arose during the investigation? How were these problems overcome? Does the children's recording portray what happened accurately? What have they found out from this investigation? What else could they investigate? Compare the results of all the groups in the class. Were similar results obtained by everyone? How many times did they test each material? What different recording methods were used? Which ones seem to be the clearest/easiest to understand? What conclusions can be drawn? How could the investigation be improved if it were repeated?

Likely problems

The children will need to be very clear at the beginning how they are going to decide whether the woodlouse is successful in moving over the material – walks the whole length, doesn't fall over, and so on. If this is not agreed upon, the results of different groups will not be comparable. Make sure that the surfaces of the materials are sufficiently different to provide a variety of results – the inclusion of very fluffy materials will assist here. The woodlouse initially chosen may not be very active, so another one may need to be selected. This will affect the results, and thus the testing will need to begin again if it is already in progress.

It may be difficult for the children to decide why the woodlouse can walk on some surfaces more easily than on others. Ask them questions to focus their attention on the way the animal moves. Look at the structure of the body and legs. Do some materials stick to the body, thereby hampering movement? Are some surfaces too smooth for the woodlouse to grip effectively? Children are often tempted to make their results fit their predictions! Try to overcome this by avoiding the words 'right' and 'wrong' when referring to answers. Discuss how scientific experiments often produce different results from those expected, and explain that this is how many new discoveries are made.

Concepts likely to emerge

The woodlouse's ability to move will depend on its size in relation to the materials and on the way that it moves – that is, how the legs move and how the body segments work. The body of the woodlouse has several features which enable it to move easily over a wide variety of surfaces:

▲ The outer body surface is not fused together but has many segments, which allows the woodlouse to curl up and curl backwards on itself to some extent.

▲ There are joints in this exoskeleton which provide greater mobility.

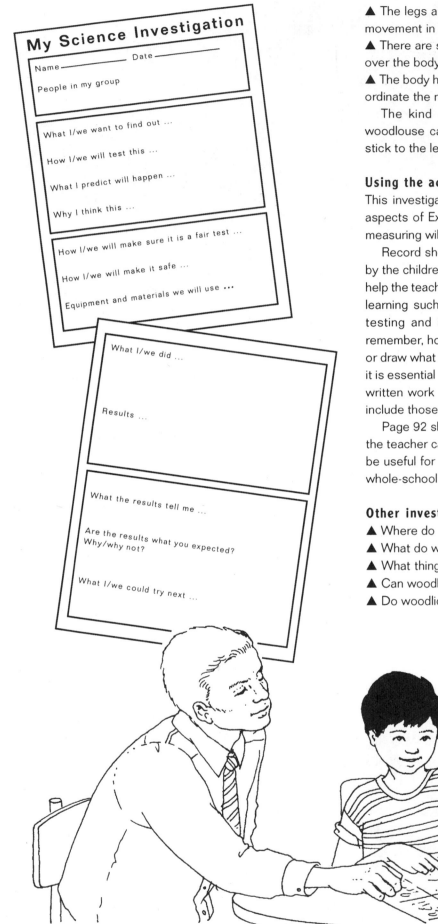

My Science Investigation

Name ———— Date ————

People in my group

What I/we want to find out …

How I/we will test this …

What I predict will happen …

Why I think this …

How I/we will make sure it is a fair test …

How I/we will make it safe …

Equipment and materials we will use …

What I/we did …

Results …

What the results tell me …

Are the results what you expected? Why/why not?

What I/we could try next …

▲ The legs are paired and jointed, permitting a diversity of movement in a variety of environments.
▲ There are small, striated (rapidly contracting) muscles all over the body, allowing rapidity of movement.
▲ The body has a variety of sense organs and a brain to co-ordinate the movements, allowing rapid responses.

The kind of surface has an effect on how well the woodlouse can move on it, because some materials may stick to the legs, give way or allow no grip.

Using the activity for assessment

This investigation should enable the teacher to assess all aspects of Experimental and Investigative Science, though measuring will not necessarily be used.

Record sheets like those shown on the left can be used by the children to organise their investigation, and may also help the teacher to assess different aspects of the children's learning such as use of predictions, understanding of fair testing and interpretation of results. It is important to remember, however, that children do not always write about or draw what they see or understand in an accurate way; so it is essential for the teacher to talk to individuals about their written work and to annotate their writing, if necessary, to include those ideas and concepts not recorded by the child.

Page 92 shows an example of an annotation form, which the teacher can attach to the child's completed work. It may be useful for inclusion in pupil profiles, and may assist with whole-school moderation of science work.

Other investigations

▲ Where do woodlice prefer to live?
▲ What do woodlice prefer to eat?
▲ What things might affect how fast woodlice can move?
▲ Can woodlice climb slopes?
▲ Do woodlice prefer the dark to the light?

OURSELVES

What might make a difference to how far I can jump?

†† *Pairs or small groups.*

🕐 *60–120 minutes.*

⚠ *Jumping activities must be carried out safely (see below).*

Key background information

Many things could affect how far a person can jump, including: the floor surface, what footwear the person is wearing, what clothing the person is wearing, the length of their legs, how the person travels through the air, the person's size and weight, how fit and active the person is, and whether the person has a run-up or not.

Preparation

Make sure that there is a suitable place where the children can carry out the investigation in safety.

Resources needed

Record sheets (if needed), landing mats, a measuring tape or ruler, chalk, pencils, a large open space.

What to do

A discussion about animals which are able to jump may be a good way to introduce the investigation. Ask the children to name animals which can jump. Select one of these, such as a rabbit or a frog, to use as the basis for more detailed questions such as: What do these animals have that help them to jump well? Why are their back legs longer than their front legs? Why do these animals need to be able to jump? Are their feet specially adapted to help with taking off and

landing? Would the muscles in their back legs need to be stronger than those in their front legs? Why?

Then ask the children to think about how humans jump. Which parts of the body do they use? Which part is used the most? In what ways do our legs compare with the back legs of rabbits or frogs? What are the differences between the muscles in our legs and those in our arms? What might be the reason for these differences?

Explain to the children that they are going to find out more about how we jump. Tell them that you want them to find out what things might make a difference to how far we can jump. Working in pairs, the children could write down all the things they think might make a difference. The whole class, or small groups, can then compare lists and come to an agreement on which factor to investigate. You may decide that each group should investigate the same thing, so that their results can be compared; or that each group should investigate something different, in order to test out more of the children's ideas. The easiest things to investigate might include length of leg, type of footwear and type of clothing worn.

As the children are planning what to do, talk to each pair or group about how they will carry out the investigation. What do they predict will happen? Why? How can they make sure the test will be fair? Which things will need to be kept the same each time? What will need to be changed? How many times do they think they should repeat the test? Are there any safety considerations? What equipment and materials will they need? How do they intend to record what happens? Have they decided on the type of jump they wish to test? Are they jumping with their feet together, or are they taking a run-up? What sort of arm movements will be used? How will they know the point from which to start measuring for each jump? Will they mark the landing-place in some way?

How many times will each person jump? What will they land on? How safe is this?

Observe the children during the investigation. Are they doing what they said they would do? If they are measuring, make sure they are using the equipment correctly. Encourage the whole group to check each other's measurements and recordings to make sure these are correct. Listen to what the children are saying as they carry out the investigation. Who is suggesting the ideas? Are all members of the group contributing? Try to involve all members by directing relevant questions to individuals.

After the investigation, ask the children to discuss the results in their groups. What do the results tell them? Were the results what they expected? If the jumps were carried out several times, should an average length of jump be recorded? What relationships are there between the factor tested (for example, length of leg) and the length of the jump? Do the children have enough evidence to support their conclusions? What problems did they encounter? How did they overcome them?

Discuss the children's recording methods. Which ones provide the clearest information? Is all the information recorded in each method? Could a graph be used to summarise the information? Can any overall conclusions be drawn? Could the investigation be improved if repeated?

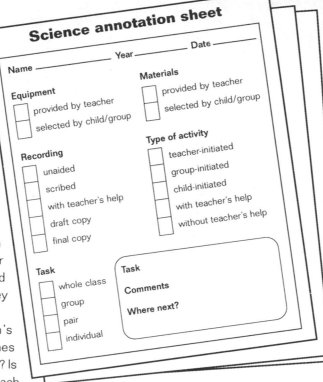

Science annotation sheet

Name _____ Year _____ Date _____

Equipment
- [ ] provided by teacher
- [ ] selected by child/group

Materials
- [ ] provided by teacher
- [ ] selected by child/group

Recording
- [ ] unaided
- [ ] scribed
- [ ] with teacher's help
- [ ] draft copy
- [ ] final copy

Type of activity
- [ ] teacher-initiated
- [ ] group-initiated
- [ ] child-initiated
- [ ] with teacher's help
- [ ] without teacher's help

Task
- [ ] whole class
- [ ] group
- [ ] pair
- [ ] individual

Task

Comments

Where next?

Safety needs to be considered at the outset to avoid the possibility of injuries. Make sure that the children have safety mats to land on, and that the group considers other safety aspects such as where they should do the activity and how they can ensure that the mats do not slip.

Problems may be experienced in drawing conclusions from the results. Help the children by referring them back to their original plan and their predictions. How well do the results answer the question that they were trying to investigate? For example, do all the children with the longest legs jump the furthest? Would it be best to work out an average length of jump for each person in order to compare the overall results? Help may be needed in calculating averages, and in deciding whether a graph could represent the findings more clearly.

Concepts likely to emerge

In general, the children with the longest legs will jump the furthest; but there are many other factors which can affect the results, such as the person's general fitness and experience of jumping. Tight clothing could restrict movement, and the type of footwear could affect the results when jumping after a run-up. It is unlikely that a person with legs, say, ten per cent longer than someone else's will repeatedly jump ten per cent further than the other person.

Likely problems

The initial problem will be deciding which factor to investigate, as many of the children's suggestions may be difficult to investigate in a primary classroom. The teacher will therefore need to discuss this problem with the children and help them to choose a factor which can be investigated more easily. A comparison between the length of the child's legs and the distance jumped is probably the most straightforward idea to test, and it may be a good idea to start with this and then to allow the children time to test other ideas (such as the type of clothing worn) at a later date.

It is important that the children agree on how they will jump and how they will measure the distances before they begin, in order to ensure accuracy of measurement. Support may be needed when the children are measuring, but this could be overcome by selecting the groups in such a way that each group has someone who can measure accurately.

Using the activity for assessment

This investigation should enable the teacher to assess all aspects of Experimental and Investigative Science.

Record sheets may help the children to organise their investigation, and may also help the teacher to assess such aspects as use of predictions, understanding of fair testing and interpretation of results. It is important to remember, however, that children do not always write about or draw what they see or understand in an accurate way; so it is essential for the teacher to talk to individuals about their written work and to annotate their writing, if necessary, to include the ideas and concepts that were not recorded by the child.

The figure shown above is an example of an annotation form, which the teacher can attach to the child's completed work. It may be useful for inclusion in pupil profiles, and may assist with whole-school moderation of science work.

Other investigations

▲ Do tall people jump the highest?

▲ What might make a difference to how far I can throw a tennis ball?

▲ Do the tallest people run the fastest?

▲ Do people with longer legs have a bigger stride?

▲ What might make a difference to how fast I can crawl?

⊕ FOOD

Does temperature have an effect on how soon grapes rot?

†† *Pairs or small groups.*

⊕ *45 minutes initially. 5–10 minutes for daily observations.*

▲ *Strict hygiene procedures must be observed in handling food.*

Key background information

Bacteria, moulds and yeasts cause foods to decay. Moulds grow best in dark, warm and moist conditions. Refrigeration is essential for the preservation of many foods. The cool temperature does not destroy the bacteria, but it does retard their growth rate. Freezing enables food to be kept for much longer periods, because the cells of the food are frozen hard so that they cannot be damaged, thus preserving them longer. Once the food is defrosted, however, the process of decay can begin rapidly.

Preparation

Obtain access to a fridge and freezer.

Resources

Grapes (fresh), plastic containers with lids or resealable plastic bags, adhesive labels, felt-tipped pens, pencils, a refrigerator, a freezer, record sheets (if required), newspaper, a thermometer.

What to do

Provide each group of children with a small bunch of grapes and ask them to look closely at the individual grapes. What do they notice about the colour, shapes, sizes, texture and smell? Are all the grapes the same? How do they differ? Remove some grapes from the stalks, and look at the places where they were removed. Is the grape damaged in some way? Could this damage affect how well the grape keeps over time? In what way? Ask the children if they have grapes at home sometimes. How long do they usually keep for? Tell them that you want them to investigate whether temperature affects how soon a grape will rot. Discuss this with them. What do they predict will happen to the grape if it is kept under these conditions:

▲ in a freezer?

▲ in a fridge?

▲ at room temperature?

▲ in a warm place?

Which one do they think will rot the soonest? Can they give their reasons for thinking this? How long do they think it will take? What experience do they base this on?

Discuss with the children how they will set up the investigation. What things will they need to consider? How will they ensure that one of the grapes is kept warm all of the time? Where could they place it? Could they wrap the container in something to keep it warm? How will they ensure

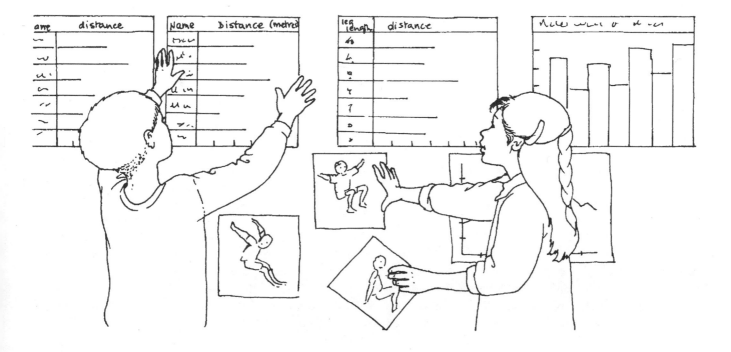

that this test is a fair one? Will the grapes used need to be the same size? Should they all be washed first? Will it be necessary to check their condition before starting the investigation? Should more than one grape be tested under each condition?

Help the children to set up the investigation, using adhesive labels to mark each container with the condition in which it is kept and the starting date. Make sure the children can read a thermometer correctly, so that they can measure the temperature in each place. Discuss how many times and in what way they will record what happens to the grapes.

Allow time each day for the children to check the grapes and record what is happening. As they are looking at the grapes, ask questions to help them consider what is going on more carefully. Has the colour of the grape changed? Where has it changed? Is the grape becoming soft in any parts? Where? What may have caused it to become soft in this area first? Do you notice anything else happening inside the container? What might have caused this? Will this have an effect on the rotting of the grape?

Once the grapes have begun to deteriorate markedly, do not let the children handle them any more. Ask them to make their observations by looking through the container's sides instead. This will ensure that they do not come into contact with the bacteria and moulds which may be present.

After a week or so, discuss the findings of the investigation. What reasons can the children give to explain why the grapes kept in a cool place lasted longer than those kept in a warm place? If the grape in the freezer is removed from there and left out at room temperature, what do they predict will happen to it? Try this and see. What does this investigation tell the children about looking after food? Where could food best be kept if you didn't have a refrigerator?

Discuss the ways in which the children recorded their findings. Were tables and/or graphs used? How well do such diagrams help in drawing conclusions? Was enough evidence collected to answer the original question? How do the results of different groups compare? What could be investigated next?

Likely problems

Ensure that other people within the school are aware of this investigation, so that the food is not inadvertently thrown out or moved to another place! The temperature of each place may need to be measured over several days, as the thermometer will need time to stabilise. It may be best to measure the temperature of the freezer overnight and then place the thermometer in the fridge for a day. Room temperature and the temperature of the warm place could then be measured the next day.

The most difficult problem may be to find a warm place to use, as sunny positions vary within the day and radiators are not on all the time. One way of overcoming this is to wrap the container in an insulating material such as newspaper. You will need to consider how this may affect the results, however, since it will change the outside surface of the container. Will this matter?

Concepts likely to emerge

Temperature affects the rate at which food rots. The lower the temperature, the more slowly the food deteriorates. This is because bacteria and moulds need warmth to grow. Warm conditions create condensation; and as all living things require water to grow, this helps the bacteria and moulds to grow more vigorously. Cooler temperatures slow down the growth of bacteria and moulds. Once food is removed from the freezer, the warmer temperature causes it to thaw and its resulting moist condition encourages bacteria and moulds to grow.

Using the activity for assessment

This investigation should enable the teacher to assess all aspects of Experimental and Investigative Science.

Record sheets similar to those shown on page 90 may help the children to organise their investigation, and may also help the teacher to assess such aspects as use of predictions, understanding of fair testing and interpretation of results. It is important to remember, however, that children do not always write about or draw what they see or understand in an accurate way; so it is essential for the teacher to talk to individuals about their written work and to

annotate their writing, if necessary, to include those ideas and concepts not recorded by the child.

Page 92 shows an annotation form, which the teacher can attach to the child's completed work. It may be useful for inclusion in pupil profiles, and may assist with whole-school moderation of science work.

Other investigations
▲ What type of container will keep food fresh for longer?
▲ How can crisps be prevented from going soft?
▲ Does light have an effect on how soon food rots?
▲ Do some foods rot sooner than others?
▲ Does washed food keep longer than unwashed food?

FLOWERS

What might make a difference to how long cut flowers remain in good condition?

✝✝ *Pairs or small groups.*

🕐 *45–60 minutes to set up. 5–10 minutes daily for observations.*

⚠ *Teacher supervision will be needed when using the knife.*

Key background information
Flowering plants need sunlight, water and nutrients from the soil to grow well. The flowers contain the reproductive organs of the plant. Most flowers contain both male and female parts.

Resources needed
Some cut flowers such as carnations, water, a measuring jug, some jars (all the same size), adhesive labels, pencils, a cut flower food sachet, a teaspoon, a knife, record sheets similar to those shown on page 90 (if required).

What to do
Show the bunch of flowers to the children. Look closely at one of the flowers and discuss the names of the flower parts. Ask the children to tell you what things they think a flower needs to grow in the garden. How long do they think flowers will last if they are cut and brought indoors? Tell them that they are going to carry out an investigation to find this out.

Ask the children to think of the things which may affect how long flowers last when cut. Some suggestions might include: changing the water every day; cutting the stem at an angle; putting plant food in the water; placing the flower in a cool or warm place; providing no water; and so on. Decide which of the things the children would like to test, and discuss with them how they could set up the investigation. Will they all investigate the same thing, or each choose a different factor? What do they predict will happen to the flowers in each case? Can they give a reason why? How will they ensure the test is fair? (Flowers with stems of the same length, the same number of flowers on each stem, the same amount of water in each jar, the same size jars.)

Make sure they label each jar with the date and basic details, and help with measuring the water if necessary. Discuss with the children how they think they will record the results and how many times a day they need to make an observation. Allow the children time each day to make their observations, and help them with their investigation by asking such questions as: Has the flower changed colour at all? Where on the flower has the colour changed? Is the stem still firm? Have the petals changed in any way? Is the flower standing upright? Has the water changed in any way? What may have caused this? Have any closed buds opened? Has the size of the flowers changed? Do the leaves look any different?

After several weeks, can the children come to any conclusions about what they have observed? Have they

LIFE PROCESSES AND LIVING THINGS

collected enough evidence to answer the initial question? Were the results what they expected? How do the results of different groups compare? Can they decide on the factors which help cut flowers to last longer? What reasons can they suggest to explain how these conditions help the flowers to last longer? Does this help us to understand how flowers survive in nature?

Discuss the various methods of recording used by the children. Which methods appear to be the most successful? Why is this? What problems did the children encounter, and how did they overcome them? How could the method of investigation be improved if the activity were repeated? What could the children investigate next?

Likely problems

The children may find it difficult to describe the changes in the flowers from day to day. Help them by making sure that they make very detailed observations of the flowers at the outset, when they are fresh. Ask them to record the colours, shapes and sizes of the flower heads, stems and leaves. They could measure the diameters of the flowers in order to ascertain the level of growth or shrinkage which may occur. Ask them to feel the petals, stem and leaves gently and to make a note of the texture and firmness, in order to make comparisons later on. It may help to take photographs of the flowers every few days. This will help the children to remember what they looked like at each stage, and will be a permanent record of what has happened.

Concepts likely to emerge

Flowers kept in the following way will tend to last longer: changing the water daily, keeping them in a cool place, adding plant food to the water, cutting the stem at an angle.

A flower kept in a cool place will stay fresh longer, because the lower temperature slows down the flower's life processes. If a flower is kept in a draught, there is an increase in water loss through transpiration. This means that there is a greater risk of the cell tissues losing water and rigidity, causing the flower to wilt.

Direct sunlight increases the temperature of the plant,

which causes greater water loss through transpiration, which results in wilting. The higher temperature also increases the rate of life processes, and so the flower runs through its display cycle in a shorter time (wilts more quickly). The children might compare this with the effects of increased temperature on the life processes of animals (including humans).

Dirty water contains many tiny spores of bacteria and fungi. If the water is not changed each day, the spores multiply rapidly, forming a barrier over the stem of the flower. This will prevent water from entering the stem. Changing the water every day, or making a new cut on the stem, minimises the effect of these spores.

Cutting the stem at an angle increases the surface area of the cut stem, allowing water to enter more rapidly. Commercial plant food contains nutrients which help the flower to stay fresh longer.

Using the activity for assessment

This investigation should enable the teacher to assess all aspects of Experimental and Investigative Science.

Record sheets (see page 90) may help the children to organise their investigation, and may also help the teacher to assess such aspects as use of predictions, understanding of fair testing and interpretation of results. It is important to remember, however, that children do not always write about or draw what they see or understand in an accurate way; so it is essential for the teacher to talk to individuals about their written work and to annotate their writing, if necessary, to include those ideas and concepts not recorded by the child.

Page 92 shows an example of an annotation form, which the teacher can attach to the child's completed work. It may be useful for inclusion in pupil profiles, and may assist with whole-school moderation of science work.

Other investigations

▲ What things make a difference to how well a bean plant grows?
▲ Do taller flowers have thicker stems?
▲ Do bees prefer certain types of flowers?

Assessment

The activities in this section can be used for summative assessment. They relate to the tasks on photocopiable pages 139 to 157, and correspond to the main areas of study covered earlier in this book.

The activities can be presented as individual tasks to provide ongoing evaluation of the children's progress, or all together at the end of a whole unit or Key Stage 2. They have been designed to stimulate individual responses, so that the whole class can work on the sheets at the same time. Alternatively, the teacher could work with individual children, especially if the child needs assistance with reading and writing; or the children could work on the activities in small groups.

Information about the PoS to be assessed, likely outcomes and reinforcement suggestions are presented individually for each activity. The time needed for each task varies from about two to ten minutes; but some children may need longer, especially if teacher support is required.

The activities will provide the teacher with a form of summative assessment, which will assist in determining individual children's overall level of achievement. They will also enable the teacher to assess those areas which may need reinforcement work, and will thus help to determine future requirements for planning.

Used in conjunction with the formative assessment activities outlined in the rest of this book, these activities will help the teacher to provide feedback on progress to the children and parents, as well as helping to determine the next step in planning for the child's learning.

The activities could also be kept as part of a pupil profile to assist the child's current (or subsequent) teacher in determining starting-points for individual pupil planning.

LIVING THINGS AND THEIR ENVIRONMENT

ACTIVITY 1
PoS to be addressed
To identify a range of common animals.
Likely outcome
Answers: robin, spider, goldfish, fox, housefly.
Reinforcement suggestions
Cut out some pictures of common animals and stick them on to card. Write the names of the animals on separate pieces of card, then ask the child to match the picture to the name. Make an ABC book of common animals.

ACTIVITY 2
PoS to be addressed
To observe and describe an animal.
Likely outcome
Names of body parts should be mentioned, such as head, body, wings and legs. Other details such as wing and body shape could also be mentioned. Some children may extend this further and include terms such as abdomen, thorax, compound eyes and antennae, as well as listing the number of legs and wings.
Reinforcement suggestions
Ask the children to observe and write down details about classroom pets such as tadpoles, goldfish or hamsters. Encourage them to describe such things as the number, shapes and names of body parts as well as observing colours, textures and movement.

ACTIVITY 3
PoS to be addressed
Living things can be grouped according to observable similarities and differences.
Likely outcome
The animals could be grouped in these ways: with wings (fly, bee, butterfly) and without wings (woodlouse, ant, silverfish); with six legs (fly, ant, bee, silverfish, butterfly) and with many legs (woodlouse). Other sortings may be valid, as long as the children can provide sound reasons for them.
Reinforcement suggestions
Cut out pictures of animals and stick these on to card. Ask the children to sort the animals into groups and to explain the criterion by which they have grouped them. Ask them to sort the same pictures in as many different ways as they can.

ACTIVITY 4
PoS to be addressed
Animals need particular conditions in order to grow and survive.
Likely outcome
The kitten needs food, water/milk and a warm bed to grow and stay healthy.
Reinforcement suggestions
Ask the children to make checklists of the things needed to care for particular pets. Discuss the results and make particular reference to the importance of food, water and shelter for all living things.

ACTIVITY 5
PoS to be addressed
Living things grow and reproduce.
Likely outcome
Correct numbering – top row: 2, 4, 6, 1; bottom row: 7, 8, 3, 5.
Reinforcement suggestions
Obtain some frog spawn or other small animals which develop quickly, such as mealworm beetles. Ask the children to keep a diary of the changes which take place each day as the animal develops to maturity.

ACTIVITY 6
PoS to be addressed
Different plants and animals are found in different habitats.
Likely outcome
Answers: whale – ocean; frog – pond; badger – wood; stickleback – pond; fox – wood; water beetle – pond; thrush – wood; octopus – ocean.
Reinforcement suggestions
Draw or cut out pictures of animals from different habitats and stick these on to card. Ask the children to sort the animals according to the habitats in which they live. Make a visit to two different habitats to compare the living things found at each site.

ACTIVITY 7
PoS to be addressed
To recognise living and non-living things.
Likely outcome
Answers: cat, fish, human, bird and tree.
Reinforcement suggestions
Ask the children to compare two things, one living and one non-living, and then to make a list of what the things look like and are able to do. What things can the living thing do that the non-living thing cannot?

LIFE PROCESSES AND LIVING THINGS

ACTIVITY 8
PoS to be addressed
To know the difference between living and non-living things.
Likely outcome
All living things feed, move (plants move by changing the direction of their growth in response to light and other factors), breathe, grow and reproduce.
Reinforcement suggestions
Visit a garden or wildlife area. Ask the children to draw or list the living and non-living things seen there. Discuss the lists once you are back in the classroom. Ask the children how they can tell if something is living or not. Agree on a list of what all living things have in common.

ACTIVITY 9
PoS to be addressed
How animals are suited to their environment.
Likely outcome
Fish are suited to their environment in the following ways: they have gills to help them breathe in water; they have fins to help them swim; they lay eggs which can float in water; their bodies are streamlined to help movement through water; they have scales which help to waterproof their bodies.
Reinforcement suggestions
Set up a freshwater tank containing goldfish in the classroom. Ask the children to observe and record how the fish breathe, feed and move. Discuss how these things help the fish to live in water.

ACTIVITY 10
PoS to be addressed
There are life processes, including nutrition, movement, growth and reproduction, that are common to all animals including humans.
Likely outcome
Answers: all these things need food, breathe, grow and need water.
Reinforcement suggestions
Ask individual children to make a list of all the things plants need to live. Discuss the results and agree on a final list. Then ask the children to do the same for animals. Compare the two lists and decide what all living things need in order to survive and grow.

ACTIVITY 11
PoS to be addressed
Animals and plants can be identified and assigned to groups using keys.

Likely outcome
Answers: A = worm; B = butterfly; C = woodlouse; D = crane-fly.
Reinforcement suggestions
Draw or cut out pictures of different minibeasts from magazines. Ask the children to write down a list of the body parts for five of these animals. The list should include the name, number and shape of each body part. Make up an identification key from this list, or ask the children to design their own key.

ACTIVITY 12
PoS to be addressed
Food chains show feeding relationships within an ecosystem. Nearly all food chains start with green plants.
Likely outcome
The children need to demonstrate that they know that the algae are eaten by the snail, which in turn is eaten by the water beetle, which is eaten by the roach, which is eaten by the heron. The term *food chain* might be mentioned, and some children may also suggest that most food chains begin with green plants. The children's examples should begin with a green plant and include one or two animals to show a feeding relationship.
Reinforcement suggestions
Cut out pictures or make written labels showing the names of common plants and animals. Ask the children to place them in food chains showing feeding relationships. Compare the results, making sure that everyone agrees on the correct outcome. Use reference books to check information if necessary.

ACTIVITY 13
PoS to be addressed
Food chains show feeding relationships within an ecosystem. Nearly all food chains start with green plants.
Likely outcome
The answers to this activity may vary considerably. They should, however, make reference to the feeding relationships between animals and plants, and the terms *food chain, predator* and *prey* may be used. Reference to the importance of green plants as the source of food for other living things could also be made.
Reinforcement suggestions
Make a study of one plant, such as wheat, and discuss how it grows and which animals (including humans) can benefit from it.

LIFE PROCESSES
AND LIVING THINGS

 PLANTS

ACTIVITY 1
PoS to be addressed
To identify a range of common plants and plant parts.
Likely outcome
Answers: leaf, flower, tree, grass.
Reinforcement suggestions
Draw or cut out pictures of common plants and plant parts from magazines. Stick these on to card. Write the names of the plants and plant parts on other pieces of card, and ask the children to match up the pictures with the correct names. Use real plants to reinforce the names further.

ACTIVITY 2
PoS to be addressed
To observe and describe a plant.
Likely outcomes
The children should describe the shape and number of the leaves and point out that the plant has a flower. Some children may also describe the stem and the plant shape. The plant is a flowering cactus.
Reinforcement suggestions
Provide the children with a variety of house plants. Discuss the names of the plant parts and encourage the children to describe the plant in terms of size, shapes, colours, textures, number of plant parts, type of leaf edge, pattern of leaf veins, type of stem, and so on.

ACTIVITY 3
PoS to be addressed
Living things can be grouped according to observable similarities and differences.
Likely outcome
The leaves could be sorted in the following ways: with smooth edges and with jagged edges; single and paired (or multiple) leaves; with pointy leaf end and with round leaf end; with many veins and with few veins. Other sortings may be valid, as long as the children can provide sound reasons for them.

ACTIVITY 4
PoS to be addressed
Plant growth is affected by the availability of light and water, and by temperature. Water and nutrients are taken in through the roots.
Likely outcome
The plant with sunlight, soil and water will grow well.

Reinforcement suggestions
Try to grow plants under the four different sets of conditions described in the activity. Ask the children to make a diary of their observations of the plants, noting how well each of them is growing.

ACTIVITY 5
PoS to be addressed
Plant growth is affected by the availability of light and water, and by temperature. Water and nutrients are taken in through the roots. Plants need light to produce food for growth.
Likely outcome
The children need to state clearly that plants need sunlight, nutrients from soil and water in order to grow well. Some children may mention that plants are able to produce their own food using sunlight, carbon dioxide and water, plus chlorophyll in the leaves (photosynthesis).
Reinforcement suggestions
Ask the children to write or draw a checklist showing what plants need to grow well. Use the checklist to monitor the plants in the classroom. Do they receive all the things they need to grow well?

ACTIVITY 6
PoS to be addressed
Plants grow and reproduce.
Likely outcome
Correct numbering – top row: 4, 6, 1, 7; bottom row: 2, 8, 3, 5.
Reinforcement suggestions
Grow some broad bean plants from seeds and make a diary record of their growth.

ACTIVITY 7
PoS to be addressed
Different plants are found in different habitats.
Likely outcome
Answers: reeds – pond; oak tree – wood; bluebells – wood; water lily – pond.
Reinforcement suggestions
Visit a pond and a wood and compare the plants growing at each site.

ACTIVITY 8
PoS to be addressed
To show an understanding of how altering one condition can affect the growth of a plant.
Likely outcome
The children need to stress the importance of sunlight to green plants, and understand that without sunlight the plant will gradually wither and die. Some children might state that sunlight is necessary for green plants to make their own food.

Reinforcement suggestions

Carry out the experiment shown in the activity. Ask the children to record what happens to the plant. Can they suggest why this happens?

ACTIVITY 9

PoS to be addressed

To recognise living and non-living things.

Likely outcome

Answers: flower, tree.

Reinforcement suggestions

Ask the children to compare a tree with a piece of wooden furniture. What makes the tree a living thing? Why is the wood no longer living?

ACTIVITY 10

PoS to be addressed

To understand the difference between living and non-living things.

Likely outcome

All living things feed, move (plants move by changing their direction of growth in response to light and other factors), breathe, grow and reproduce.

Reinforcement suggestions

Ask the children to write down ten living and ten non-living things and then to show their lists to others. Do the others agree with the things on each child's list? What characteristics do all ten living things on a list have in common?

ACTIVITY 11

PoS to be addressed

To know the names of flowering plant parts.

Likely outcome

Correct plant names – left: stamen, pistil; leaf; stem; right: petal, sepal, root.

Reinforcement suggestions

Use some flowering house plants to discuss the names of the plant parts with the children. Write the names down. Then cut out some drawings of the plant parts and ask the children to match up the names with the drawings.

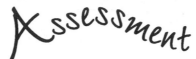

ACTIVITY 12

PoS to be addressed

Plants need light to produce food for growth. The leaves are very important in this process. The root anchors the plant; water and nutrients are taken in through the root and transported through the stem to other parts of the plant. The life cycle of flowering plants.

Likely outcome

The roots anchor the plant and help with the intake of water and nutrients from the soil. Stems conduct water and nutrients from the roots to other parts of the plant, conduct food produced in the leaves to other plant parts, provide support for the leaves and produce and support the flowers and fruit. The leaves produce food for the plant by combining carbon dioxide and water, using sunlight energy absorbed by chlorophyll in the leaves (photosynthesis). The leaves also allow the plant to lose water it does not need above ground and so maintain the upward flow of water and minerals (transpiration). The flowers are the reproductive organs of the plant. They attract insects, which help in pollination. After pollination, the flowers dry up and a seed head is formed. The seeds are then dispersed and new flowers grow.

Reinforcement suggestions

Use cut flowers to name and describe the functions of flower parts. Allow the children to observe the flowers closely, looking at colours, shapes and textures. Discuss why flowers are colourful and scented, and how insects help to pollinate flowers.

ACTIVITY 13

PoS to be addressed

Animals and plants can be identified and assigned to particular groups using keys.

Likely outcome

Answers: A = lily; B = daisy; C = grass; D = oak tree.

Reinforcement suggestions

Cut out pictures of a variety of plants and stick them on to card. Tell the children to write down questions they could ask about each of the plants and use these questions to write a key for the plant pictures.

ACTIVITY 14

PoS to be addressed

Food chains show feeding relationships (between living things) in an ecosystem. Nearly all food chains begin with green plants.

Likely outcome

The children could either describe the feeding relationships or draw food chains which include one or all of the following: grain – mouse – fox; grass – rabbit – fox; grass – rabbit – human. The children might also recognise the fact that nearly all food chains begin with green plants.

Reinforcement suggestions

Visit a pond and observe the feeding relationships there. Ask the children to draw food chains showing these relationships.

LIFE PROCESSES
AND LIVING THINGS

ACTIVITY 15

PoS to be addressed

Food chains show feeding relationships in an ecosystem. Nearly all food chains begin with green plants.

Likely outcome

Answers to this question are likely to vary considerably, but the children should mention the importance of plants as food producers for other living things. The children might also mention that plants are used as shelter by some animals and that humans use plants to make things.

Reinforcement suggestions

Revise how plants make their own food through photosynthesis by discussing the process with the children. Then ask the children to draw or list other ways in which plants can be used by other living things. A group discussion will help to generate ideas.

ACTIVITY 16

PoS to be addressed

The life cycle of flowering plants.

Likely outcome

Correct numbering – top row: 1, 2, 7, 5; bottom row: 3, 6, 4, 8.

Reinforcement suggestions

Revise plant pollination, seed production, seed dispersal and germination through small-group discussions. Grow flowering plants, such as broad bean plants, to observe each stage of the cycle.

ACTIVITY 17

PoS to be addressed

The life cycle of flowering plants

Likely outcome

The petals attract insects to the plant, thereby aiding pollination. The stigma is the part of the female reproductive organs (pistil) on which the pollen lands. The pollen grows a tube which passes down the style into the ovary, where the eggs are. Here the male cell joins with the female egg to produce seeds. The stamen is the male reproductive organ, consisting of an anther and a filament. Pollen forms on the anther.

Reinforcement suggestion

Cut up flowers to look at the different plant parts. Discuss their functions.

ACTIVITY 18

PoS to be addressed

To compare the flowering plant life cycle with the human life cycle.

Likely outcome

The children should mention the fact that both of these cycles require a male cell and a female egg to unite in order for a new organism to be created. Flowering plants and humans thus need both male and female elements in order to reproduce themselves.

Reinforcement suggestions

Cut out pictures of flowering plants and humans, showing the different stages of their life cycles. Ask the children to place the pictures in order for each cycle. Then ask them to make comparisons between the stages of development in flowers and in humans.

ACTIVITY 19

PoS to be addressed

Plants are suited to the particular environment in which they grow.

Likely outcome

Cacti have thick, fleshy leaves to help them conserve water. Some have spikes or hairs which help to provide shade on the plant, thus reducing transpiration. Cacti will only flower if they receive a lot of sunlight. Trees grow tall to obtain the maximum amount of sunlight by reaching above the undergrowth in woods. They have very long roots to tap the water supply underground. The water lily has large leaves to create a large surface area for sunlight to fall on. The leaves float on water to ensure maximum exposure to sunlight. The water lily has long roots and a firm stem to anchor it in the water.

Reinforcement suggestions

Visit two different habitats and compare the plants living in each. Make a list of the things which help each plant to survive in its environment.

OURSELVES

ACTIVITY 1

PoS to be addressed

To name the parts of the human body.

Likely outcome

Answers: head, neck, chest, arm, hand, leg, knee, foot.

Reinforcement suggestions

Draw body parts and write the corresponding names on individual pieces of card. Ask the children to match up the pictures with the words.

ACTIVITY 2

PoS to be addressed

Humans need food, water and shelter to survive.

Likely outcome

Answers: fresh water, food and shelter.

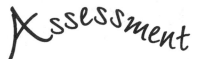

Reinforcement suggestions

Ask the children to make a list of all the things they do in one day. Ask them to work in pairs to decide which of the things on the list are essential and which are not. Compare their results with those of others. Discuss how important it is to eat and drink and to have somewhere to live. What might happen to you if you could not have these things?

ACTIVITY 3

PoS to be addressed

The human life cycle.

Likely outcome

Correct numbering – top row: 1, 4, 2; bottom row: 3, 6, 5.

Reinforcement suggestions

Ask the children to bring in photographs of themselves and other members of their families at different ages. Can other children put these into order, showing the development of humans from babyhood through to old age? Discuss the characteristics of each stage.

ACTIVITY 4

PoS to be addressed

Humans can be grouped according to observable similarities and differences.

Likely outcome

The people could be grouped in these ways: young and old; tall and short; thin and fat. Other sortings may be valid as long as the children can provide sound reasons for them.

Reinforcement suggestions

Cut out pictures of people from magazines and stick them on to card. Sort the people using one characteristic, such as age. Can the children guess how you have sorted them? Then ask the children to sort the pictures, using a criterion of their own, and invite others to work it out. Discuss the differences and similarities between people.

ACTIVITY 5

PoS to be addressed

There are life processes – including nutrition, movement, growth and reproduction – that are common to all animals, including humans.

Likely outcome

Answers: can grow, can move, can eat and drink, can have young, eat food that needs sunlight to grow.

Reinforcement suggestions

Show the children some pictures of adult animals, including humans, with babies. Ask them to tell you what the differences are between the animals in the pictures. Then ask them to tell you what the animals have in common. Make a list of things that all the animals can do.

ACTIVITY 6

PoS to be addressed

Humans need an adequate and varied diet to keep healthy.

Likely outcomes

Answers: vegetables, water, milk/cheese/eggs/soya, fish/meat/nuts/pulses, bread/cereals, small amounts of oil, butter or margarine, fruit.

Reinforcement suggestions

Discuss the types and amounts of foods which should be eaten to maintain good health. Ask the children to design healthy packed lunches and school dinners based on this information.

ACTIVITY 7

PoS to be addressed

How poor diet can affect the health of humans. An adequate and varied diet is needed for people to stay healthy. How changing one aspect of their living habits can affect the health of humans.

Likely outcome

The answers to these questions may vary considerably, but the main points the children should mention are: a poor diet can cause sickness and disease; eating too much of the wrong foods can cause obesity and tooth decay; exercise is important; good hygiene prevents the spread of germs and disease; and plenty of rest and sleep helps to build strong bodies. The children might also mention that it is important to avoid smoking and taking drugs, and that too much alcohol can be harmful.

Reinforcement suggestions

Ask the children to work in groups to compile a list of ten ways to stay fit and healthy. Share the results with the other groups and make a whole-class list. Discuss what might happen to the body if these things are ignored.

ACTIVITY 8

PoS to be addressed

The functions of teeth and the importance of dental care.

Likely outcome

The three things you should do to care for your teeth are: eat the right types of food, brush teeth after meals and visit the dentist regularly. Our teeth help us to bite and tear food, and to chew it so that the pieces are small enough to be swallowed. Digestion begins in the mouth when chewing food stimulates the production of saliva. Saliva helps digestion by making the food moist, so it can be swallowed more easily; and it contains a digestive enzyme which starts to break down the food.

Reinforcement suggestions

Ask the children to design posters which tell others how to care for their teeth.

ACTIVITY 9

PoS to be addressed

Humans have skeletons and muscles to support their bodies and to help them to move.

Likely outcome

The skeleton protects and supports the internal organs of the body and works together with the muscles to create movement. The muscles cover the skeleton and are attached to the bones by ligaments. Muscles cause the body to move. They work in pairs and can relax and contract. The diagram should be labelled from the top: skull, backbone, hip-bone, kneecap, ankle.

Reinforcement suggestions

Draw or photocopy a large outline diagram of the skeleton. Ask the children to make labels to attach to the skeleton, naming the main bones. Discuss how the skeleton and muscles cause the body to move.

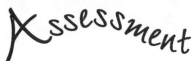

ACTIVITY 10

PoS to be addressed

The structure of the heart and how it acts as a pump to send blood around the body. How blood circulates through the arteries and veins.

Likely outcome

The name of this organ is the heart. It pumps blood around the body. The body needs a constant supply of blood because the cells need food and oxygen, which the blood supplies. The arteries carry blood away from the heart.

Reinforcement suggestions

Ask the children to find their pulse. Discuss what causes the pulse. Talk about how important it is for blood to be moved around to all parts of the body. Ask the children to tell you how they think the blood gets food and oxygen, and why these things are necessary. Look at a diagram showing a cross-section of the heart to help the children understand how it functions.

ACTIVITY 11

PoS to be addressed

The effects of exercise and rest on the pulse rate.

Likely outcome

James and Sally were investigating the effects that rest and exercise have on the pulse rate. Their results tell us that the pulse rate increases with exercise. This is because the muscles need more food and oxygen in order to do more work during exercise. The food and oxygen are supplied by the blood.

Reinforcement suggestions

Ask the children to try out the activity that James and Sally were doing. How do their own results compare with those shown on the sheet?

ACTIVITY 12

PoS to be addressed

Tobacco, alcohol and other drugs can have harmful effects.

Likely outcome

Answers: cigarettes, heroin, alcohol and someone else's tablets. Some of the other things could be harmful if not used correctly, such as aspirin, anti-depressants and sleeping tablets. Some people may be allergic to certain medicines, so these could also be harmful.

Reinforcement suggestions

Ask the children to work in pairs to make a list of things they think could be harmful to their health if they were to take them. Share the lists with the whole class and compare the answers. Agree on a whole-class list of things that could be harmful. Discuss ways of informing others about the effects of these things.

ACTIVITY 13

PoS to be addressed

The main organs of the human body and where they are found in the body.

Likely outcome

Answers: brain, heart, stomach, liver, intestines.

Reinforcement suggestions

Use a model or picture of the human body to show the children where the main organs are found. Ask the children to use reference books to find out what these organs do.

ACTIVITY 14

PoS to be addressed

Similarities between the human life cycle and the life cycle of flowering plants.

Likely outcome

The children should mention the fact that both cycles require a male cell and a female egg to unite in order for a new organism to be formed. Humans and flowering plants thus need both male and female forms in order to reproduce themselves.

Reinforcement suggestions

Ask the children to draw life cycles for both a human and a flowering plant. Discuss the similarities between the two.

Photocopiables

The pages in this section can be photocopied for use in the classroom or school which has purchased this book, and do not need to be declared in any return in respect of any photocopying licence.

They comprise a varied selection of both pupil and teacher resources, including pupil worksheets, resource material and record sheets to be completed by the teacher or children. Most of the photocopiable pages are related to individual activities in the book; the name of the activity is indicated at the top of the sheet, together with a page reference indicating where the lesson plan for that activity can be found.

Individual pages are discussed in detail within each lesson plan, accompanied by ideas for adaptation where appropriate – of course, each sheet can be adapted to suit your own needs and those of your class. Sheets can also be coloured, laminated, mounted on to card, enlarged and so on where appropriate.

Pupil worksheets and record sheets have spaces provided for children's names and for noting the date on which each sheet was used. This means that, if so required, they can be included easily within any pupil assessment portfolio.

The activities on pages 139 to 157 can be used for the purposes of summative assessment. Background notes for these activities are provided in the Assessment chapter.

LIFE PROCESSES
AND LIVING THINGS

Living or non-living?, see page 14

Living and non-living things

▲ Cut out the pictures below.
▲ Sort them into living and non-living things.

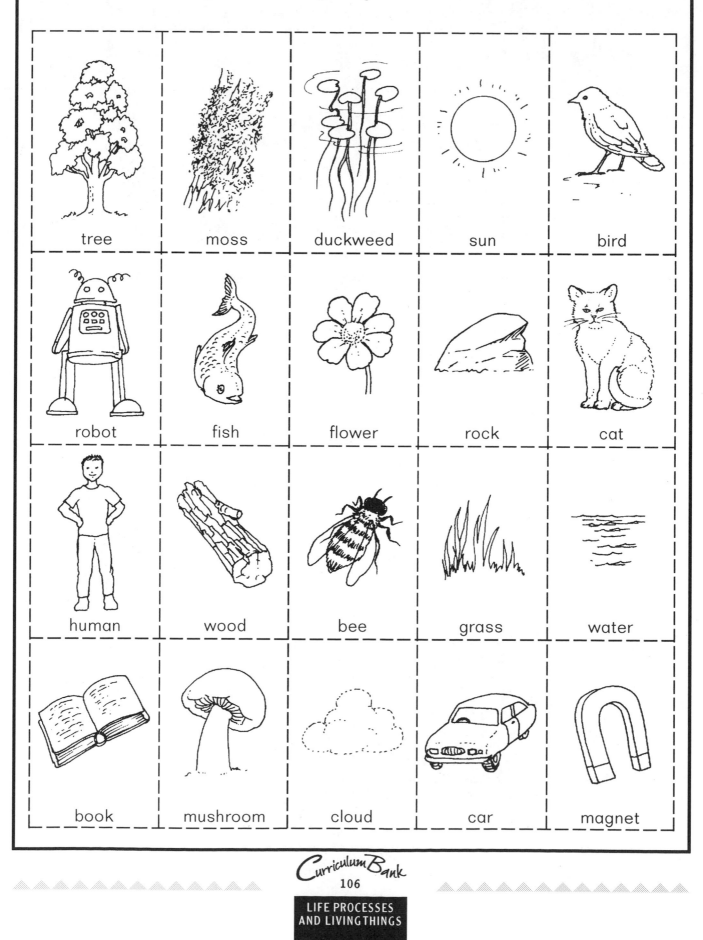

tree	moss	duckweed	sun	bird
robot	fish	flower	rock	cat
human	wood	bee	grass	water
book	mushroom	cloud	car	magnet

LIFE PROCESSES
AND LIVING THINGS

Animals and feeding

Name _____   Date _____

▲ Read each paragraph. Underline information about the animal's habitat, mouth type, teeth, food, body size and how often it eats. Use this information to complete your survey sheet.

Hedgehog

Hedgehogs are found in many countries in Europe. They sleep during the day and come out at night. Hedgehogs are between 20cm and 30cm long and weigh about 700g. They have a long snout which is used to dig for food. They eat caterpillars, beetles, worms, slugs, young mice and fruit. They tend to live in areas with bushes or shrubs, not in dense woods. The hedgehog hibernates during winter.

Emperor Penguin

This is the largest of all sea birds – length 112cm, weight 20–40kg. They live in the Antarctic. They live in large groups. They cannot fly, but are very good swimmers. They eat fish, squid and shrimps, and have a very sharp bill. They live on pack ice. The birds feed several times a day, but during the breeding season the male can go without food for up to 115 days. The male incubates the egg.

Green Turtle

This reptile is found in warm oceans and the Mediterranean Sea. It grows up to 1.5m in length and 185kg in weight. It can live to be 50 years old. It eats fish and crustaceans when young, but only eats plants when fully grown. It feeds many times a day. The turtle lays many eggs. They are buried on beaches in the sand. The Green Turtle has sharp, horny jaws, instead of teeth. It is a protected species.

Giant Panda

The Giant Panda is found in small areas of China. The male can grow to a height of 1.5m and can weigh up to 120kg. Pandas are very rare. They eat mainly bamboo, but also eat berries, fruit, flowers, fungi, grass, bark and sometimes birds' eggs. They need to eat many times each day (16 hours a day). They live in cold regions where bamboo grows. Giant pandas have large molar teeth. One of the main reasons why pandas are rare is that the areas where they live have been cleared for farming.

LIFE PROCESSES
AND LIVINGTHINGS

Animal life cycles, see page 21

Animal life cycles

▲ Cut up this sheet to make animal cards. Your teacher will tell you what to do next.

frog	shark	sparrow	cat	bee
duck-billed platypus	ostrich	elephant	kangaroo	chicken
crocodile	beetle	monkey	snake	goldfish
whale	tortoise	newt	trout	lizard

LIFE PROCESSES
AND LIVINGTHINGS

Animal life cycles

Name _____   Date _____

▲ Use books to help you find out about the life cycle of your chosen animal.

Animal name _____

Animal class (mammal, reptile, fish, amphibian, bird, insect, other)

_____

In what countries does it live? _____

In what sort of habitat does it live? _____

How many young do the adults usually have? _____

Do the adults look after the young? (If yes, say how.) _____

_____

_____

At what time of year are the young usually born? _____

_____

How long does it take the young to become adults? _____

_____

Are the young born in a special place, such as a nest? Describe it.

_____

_____

What do the young eat? _____

What do the adults eat? _____

How long does the animal usually live? _____

Write down any other interesting information about this animal. _____

_____

_____

LIFE PROCESSES
AND LIVING THINGS

Animal life cycles, see page 21

Animal life cycles

Name _____ Date _____

▲ Use books to find out about these things:

> Animal name
>
> _____

▲ Draw a picture of what your animal looks like when it is born.

▲ Draw a picture of what your animal looks like when it is young.

▲ Draw a picture of what your animal looks like when it is an adult.

▲ Write information about your animal in the space below.

LIFE PROCESSES AND LIVING THINGS

Introducing keys, see page 24

Using keys

Name _____   Date _____

▲ Use this key to name these animals.

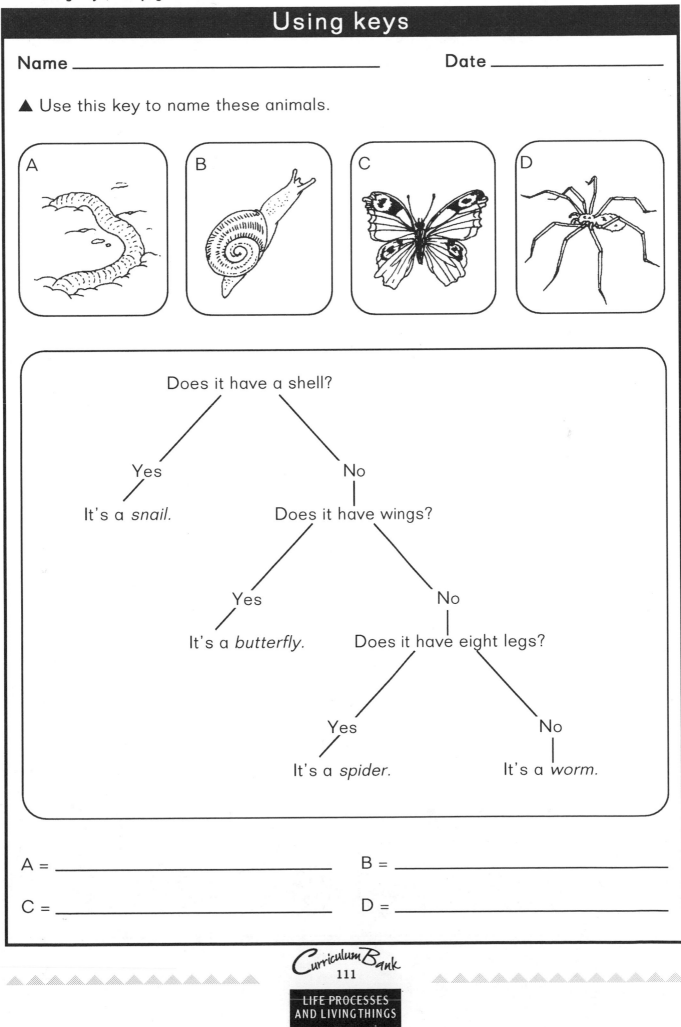

A

B

C

D

Does it have a shell?

Yes   No

It's a *snail.*   Does it have wings?

Yes   No

It's a *butterfly.*   Does it have eight legs?

Yes   No

It's a *spider.*   It's a *worm.*

A = _____   B = _____

C = _____   D = _____

Using keys

Name _____   Date _____

▲ Cut out the pictures of minibeasts at the bottom of the page and stick them in the box which you think best describes them.
▲ Compare your answers with others. Do they agree?

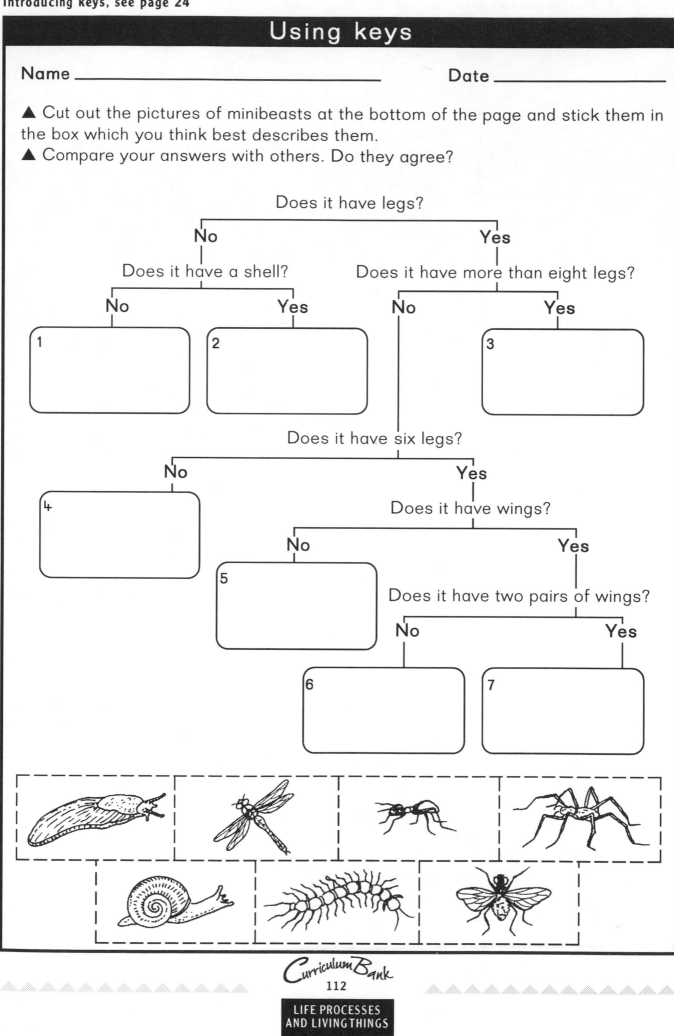

Does it have legs?

No   Yes

Does it have a shell?   Does it have more than eight legs?

No   Yes   No   Yes

[1]   [2]   [3]

Does it have six legs?

No   Yes

[4]   Does it have wings?

No   Yes

[5]   Does it have two pairs of wings?

No   Yes

[6]   [7]

Using keys in the local environment, see page 26

Plant identification key

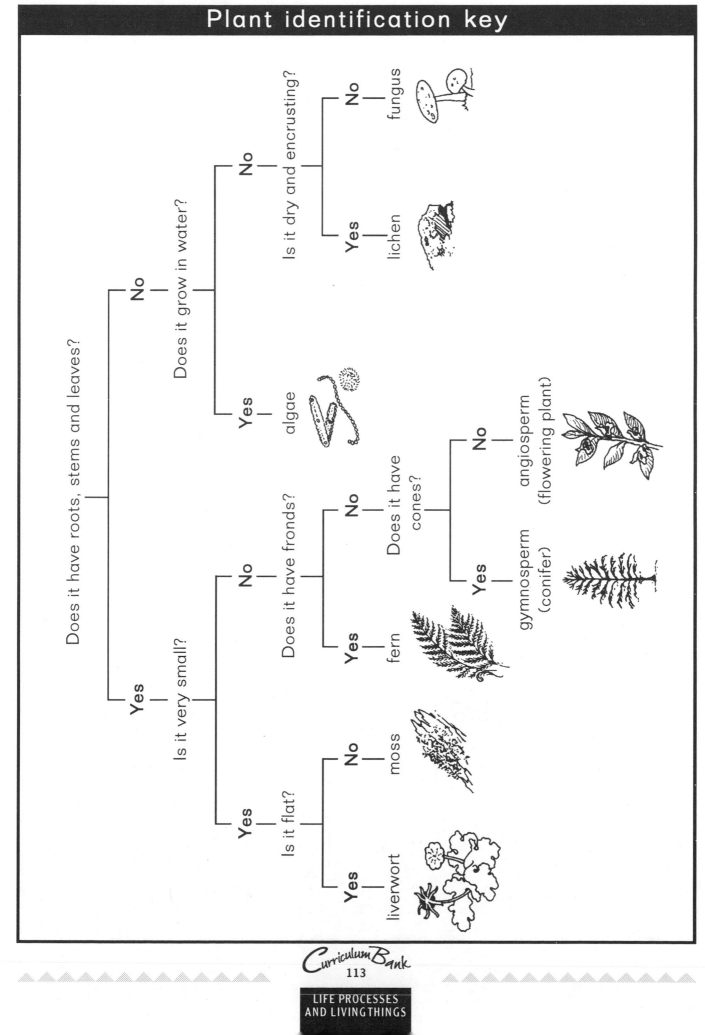

**LIFE PROCESSES
AND LIVING THINGS**

Using keys in the local environment, see page 26

Plant identification key

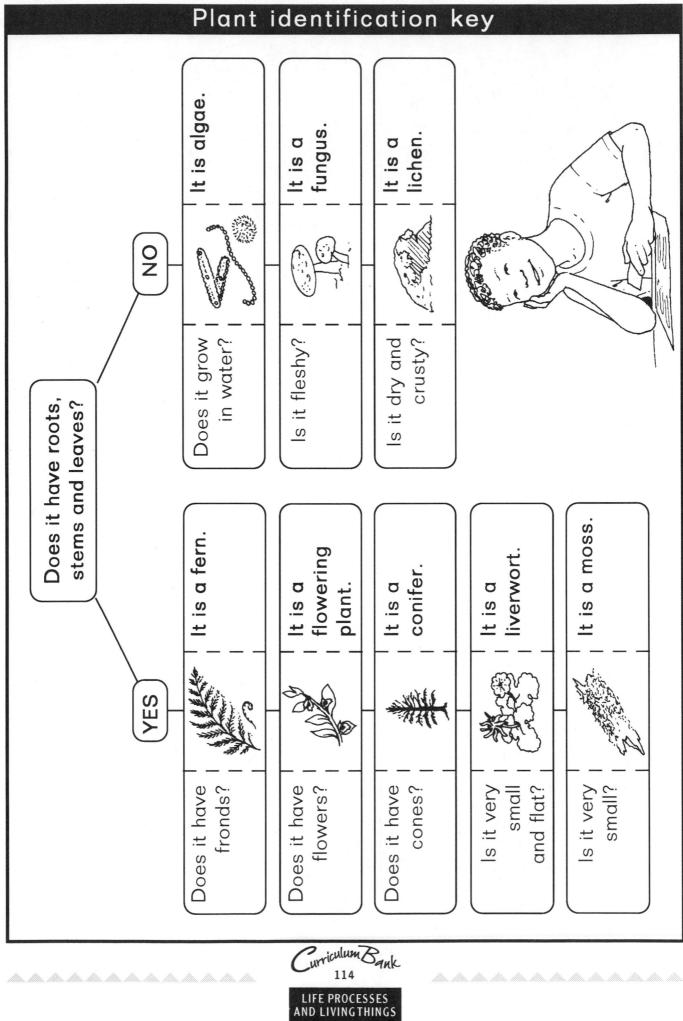

NO

It is algae.

Does it grow in water?

It is a fungus.

Is it fleshy?

It is a lichen.

Is it dry and crusty?

Does it have roots, stems and leaves?

YES

It is a fern.

Does it have fronds?

It is a flowering plant.

Does it have flowers?

It is a conifer.

Does it have cones?

It is a liverwort.

Is it very small and flat?

It is a moss.

Is it very small?

Using keys in the local environment, see page 26

Minibeast identification key

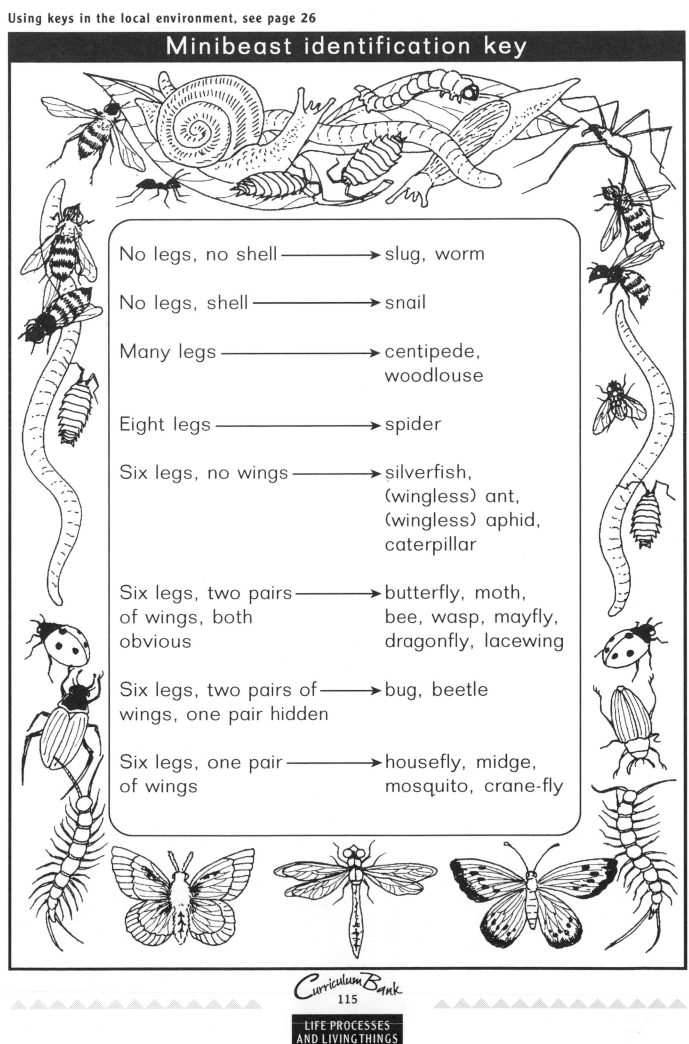

No legs, no shell ——————→ slug, worm

No legs, shell ——————→ snail

Many legs ——————→ centipede, woodlouse

Eight legs ——————→ spider

Six legs, no wings ——————→ silverfish, (wingless) ant, (wingless) aphid, caterpillar

Six legs, two pairs of wings, both obvious ——————→ butterfly, moth, bee, wasp, mayfly, dragonfly, lacewing

Six legs, two pairs of wings, one pair hidden ——————→ bug, beetle

Six legs, one pair of wings ——————→ housefly, midge, mosquito, crane-fly

LIFE PROCESSES
AND LIVING THINGS

Minibeast identification key

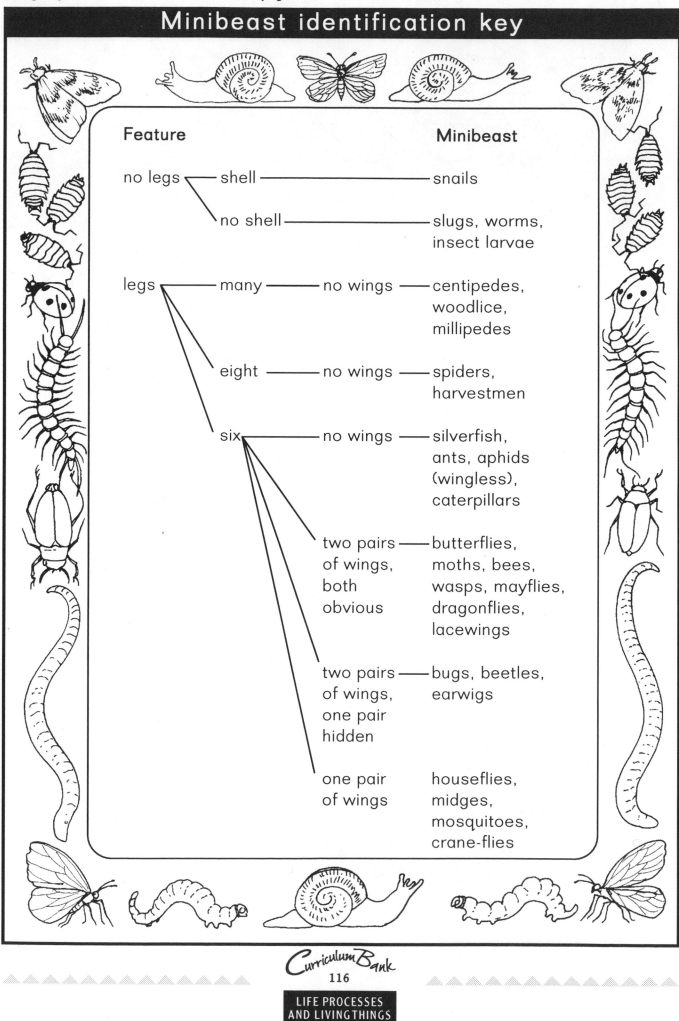

Feature			Minibeast
no legs	shell		snails
	no shell		slugs, worms, insect larvae
legs	many	no wings	centipedes, woodlice, millipedes
	eight	no wings	spiders, harvestmen
	six	no wings	silverfish, ants, aphids (wingless), caterpillars
		two pairs of wings, both obvious	butterflies, moths, bees, wasps, mayflies, dragonflies, lacewings
		two pairs of wings, one pair hidden	bugs, beetles, earwigs
		one pair of wings	houseflies, midges, mosquitoes, crane-flies

LIFE PROCESSES AND LIVING THINGS

Plants and their environment, see page 30

Comparing plants

Name _____

Date _____

	Land plant	Water plant
What are the leaves like?		
Where are the roots anchored?		
What is the stem like?		
What holds the plant up?		
How tall is the plant?		

Draw the land plant here.

Draw the water plant here.

What things make your land plant suited to the place where you found it?

What things make your water plant suited to the place where you found it?

LIFE PROCESSES
AND LIVING THINGS

Animals and their environment, see page 31

Animals and their environment (1)

▲ Cut out the animals and sentences below.
▲ Match up each sentence to the animal you think has that special feature.
Some animals may match with more than one sentence.

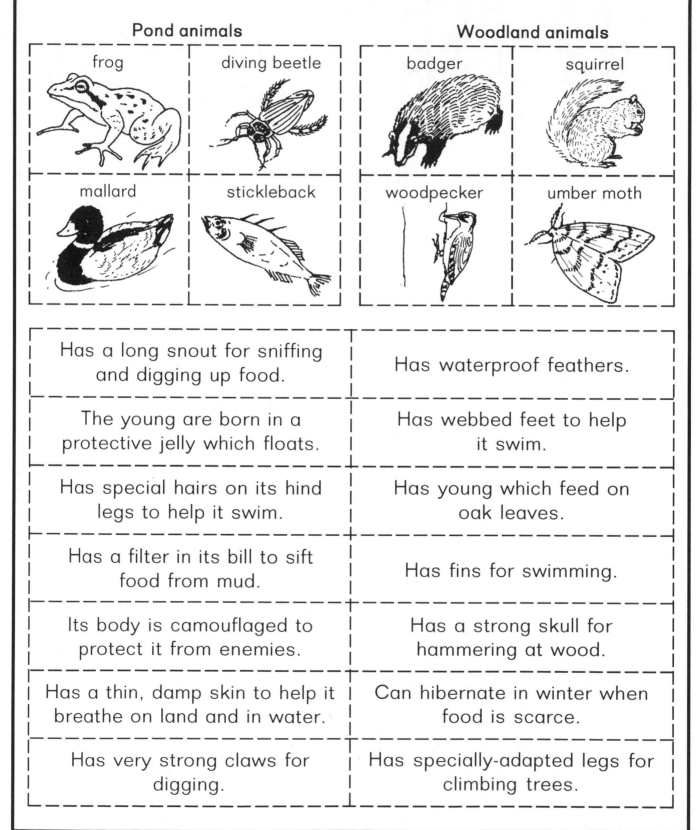

Pond animals

| frog | diving beetle |
| stickleback | mallard |

Woodland animals

| badger | squirrel |
| woodpecker | umber moth |

Has a long snout for sniffing and digging up food.	Has waterproof feathers.
The young are born in a protective jelly which floats.	Has webbed feet to help it swim.
Has special hairs on its hind legs to help it swim.	Has young which feed on oak leaves.
Has a filter in its bill to sift food from mud.	Has fins for swimming.
Its body is camouflaged to protect it from enemies.	Has a strong skull for hammering at wood.
Has a thin, damp skin to help it breathe on land and in water.	Can hibernate in winter when food is scarce.
Has very strong claws for digging.	Has specially-adapted legs for climbing trees.

LIFE PROCESSES AND LIVING THINGS

Animals and their environment (2)

Name _____

Date _____

▲ Look at the pictures. Use the information given to complete the sentences below.

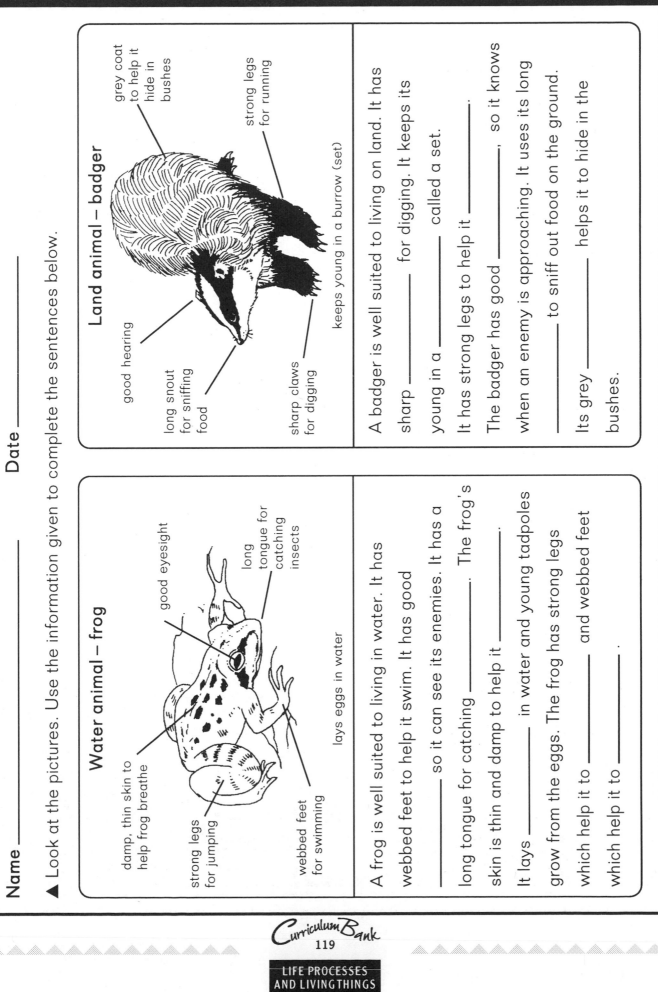

Land animal – badger

grey coat to help it hide in bushes

strong legs for running

good hearing

long snout for sniffing food

sharp claws for digging

keeps young in a burrow (set)

A badger is well suited to living on land. It has sharp _____ for digging. It keeps its young in a _____ called a set. It has strong legs to help it _____. The badger has good _____, so it knows when an enemy is approaching. It uses its long _____ to sniff out food on the ground. Its grey _____ helps it to hide in the bushes.

Water animal – frog

good eyesight

long tongue for catching insects

damp, thin skin to help frog breathe

strong legs for jumping

webbed feet for swimming

lays eggs in water

A frog is well suited to living in water. It has webbed feet to help it swim. It has good _____ so it can see its enemies. It has a long tongue for catching _____. The frog's skin is thin and damp to help it _____. It lays _____ in water and young tadpoles grow from the eggs. The frog has strong legs which help it to _____ and webbed feet which help it to _____.

How animals and plants help each other, see page 33

Oak tree life

All the things below live on or visit oak trees.
▲ Cut up this sheet to make individual cards. Sort them into two groups – those which help the tree and those which do not.

green woodpecker	nut weevil larva	lacewing
eats bark insects	eats acorns	eats aphids
grey squirrel	woodlouse	oak hook-tip moth caterpillar
carries away acorns	eats rotting wood	eats oak leaves
great tit	aphid	ladybird
eats insects	eats sap from leaves	eats aphids
bat	cross spider	green oak roller moth larva
eats moths	eats insects	eats oak leaves

LIFE PROCESSES AND LIVING THINGS

Food chains (1), see page 34

Pond food chains

Name _____

Date _____

▲ Complete the food chains below using this information.

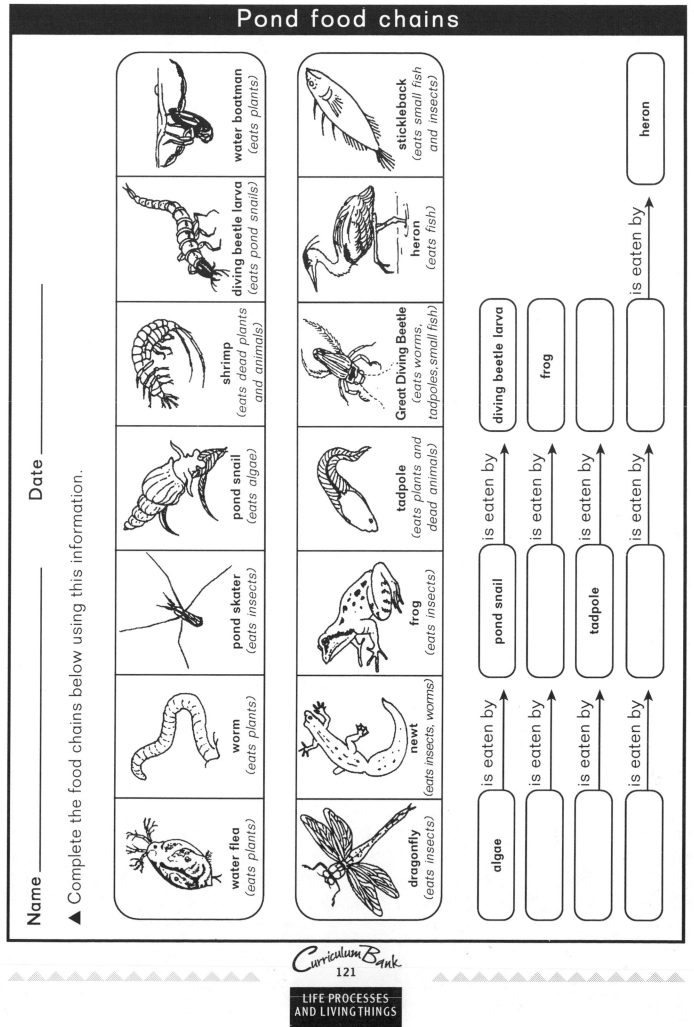

water boatman (eats plants)

diving beetle larva (eats pond snails)

shrimp (eats dead plants and animals)

pond snail (eats algae)

pond skater (eats insects)

worm (eats plants)

water flea (eats plants)

stickleback (eats small fish and insects)

heron (eats fish)

Great Diving Beetle (eats worms, tadpoles, small fish)

tadpole (eats plants and dead animals)

frog (eats insects)

newt (eats insects, worms)

dragonfly (eats insects)

algae → is eaten by → pond snail → is eaten by → diving beetle larva

□ → is eaten by → □ → is eaten by → frog

□ → is eaten by → tadpole → is eaten by → □

□ → is eaten by → □ → is eaten by → □ → is eaten by → heron

Plant variety, see page 40

Plant I-Spy

Name _____   **Date** _____

▲ Collect, draw or make rubbings of these things from the plants you see.

a pointed leaf	a damaged leaf	a round leaf
patterned bark	a flower petal	a leaf skeleton
a jagged leaf	a seed	a bumpy twig

LIFE PROCESSES AND LIVING THINGS

Plant variety, see page 40

My plant

Name _____   Date _____

A drawing of my plant

A leaf rubbing

Plant measurements:

height _____ length of leaf _____ width of leaf _____

Where I found it: _____

Special things about my plant: _____

_____

_____

Leaves: colour _____   Stem: colour _____

texture _____   texture _____

Name your plant (use books or invent a name of your own):

_____

LIFE PROCESSES
AND LIVING THINGS

Photocopiables

Plant keys, see page 42

Plant keys

1. Single leaf on a stem – go to 2.
   More than one leaf on a stem – go to 5.

2. Has a jagged edge – go to 3.
   Has a wavy edge – oak.

3. Heart-shaped – lime.
   Not heart-shaped – go to 4.

4. Has very long points – holly.
   No long points – sweet chestnut.

5. Leaves in pairs, spaced out along the stem – go to 6.
   Leaves closer together – go to 7.

6. Has smooth edges – walnut.
   Has jagged edges – ash.

7. Has needle-shaped leaves – Douglas fir.
   Has oval-shaped leaves – horse chestnut.

▲ Cut out the leaf cards below. Find out the names of the trees they belong to by using the key.

Flowering plant life cycle, see page 61

Flowering plant life cycle

▲ Cut out the picture cards below. Place them in the correct order to show how the flower grows from a seed to a mature plant.

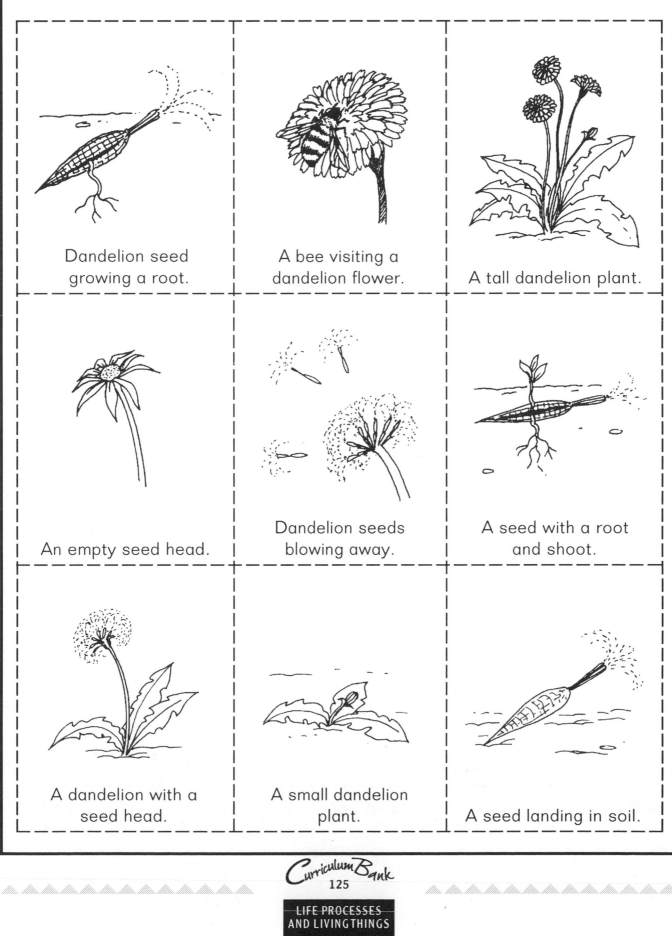

Dandelion seed growing a root.	A bee visiting a dandelion flower.	A tall dandelion plant.
An empty seed head.	Dandelion seeds blowing away.	A seed with a root and shoot.
A dandelion with a seed head.	A small dandelion plant.	A seed landing in soil.

LIFE PROCESSES
AND LIVING THINGS

My family, see page 64

My family (1)

Name _____   Date _____

▲ Stick photographs or draw pictures of your family in the spaces below.

me	parent	brother/sister
grandparent	aunt/uncle	cousin

▲ Find out these things about yourself and two other people in your family:

Feature	Me	Relative 1	Relative 2
eye colour			
hair colour			
freckles?			
dimples?			
curly or straight hair?			
long or short eyelashes?			
dark or light eyebrows?			
shape of nose			
free or attached ear lobes?			

▲ Make a list of the things that the people in your family have in common on the back of this sheet.

My family, see page 64

My family (2)

Name _____   Date _____

This is a picture of the _____ family.

This table shows the common features of this family.

Feature	Son	Mother	Father	Gran
eye colour	blue	brown	blue	blue
hair colour	fair	dark	dark	grey
freckles?	yes	no	no	no
dimples?	no	yes	no	yes
curly or straight hair?	straight	curly	curly	curly
long or short eyelashes?	long	short	long	long
dark or light eyebrows?	light	dark	dark	light

▲ Make a list of all the things the _____ family have in common.

LIFE PROCESSES
AND LIVING THINGS

My friends, see page 65

My friends

Name _____   Date _____

▲ How different are you from your friends? Complete this page to find out.

Feature	Me	_____ (Name)	_____ (Name)	_____ (Name)	_____ (Name)
height (cm)					
weight (kg)					
eye colour					
hair colour					
freckles?					
arm length (shoulder to end of 3rd finger)					
distance around wrist					
shoe size					
shortest time to run 25 metres					

Now answer these questions:

Who is the tallest? _____

What is the difference (in cm) between the shortest and the tallest person?

_____

Does everyone in the group have freckles? _____

Who has the shortest arm length? _____

Does the tallest person have the longest arm length? _____

Does the shortest person have the smallest shoe size? _____

Who can run 25 metres in the shortest time? _____

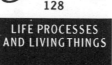
LIFE PROCESSES AND LIVING THINGS

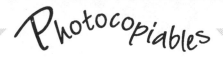

Changes in me

Name _____   Date _____

▲ How much will you grow over several months? Carry out these measurements to find out.

date	height (cm)	weight (kg)	length of foot from toe to heel (cm)	waist (cm)	wrist (cm)	length of hand 3rd fingertip to wrist (cm)	neck (cm)

▲ Use this graph to record the changes in your height.

Height in cm

Month

LIFE PROCESSES
AND LIVING THINGS

Food, see page 68

My food diary

Name _____   Date _____

▲ Use this sheet to help you complete your food diary.

Breakfast

cereal | toast | milk | tea | orange juice

Snacks

chocolate | crisps | fruit | cake | biscuits

Lunch

chips | meat/fish | sandwiches | yoghurt | fruit juice

Evening meal

vegetables | meat | potatoes/rice | fish | ice-cream | hot drink

LIFE PROCESSES
AND LIVING THINGS

Our skeleton, see page 74

My bones

Name _____   Date _____

▲ Work with a partner to measure these bones in your body, using a measuring tape. Fill in your answers on the right of this sheet.

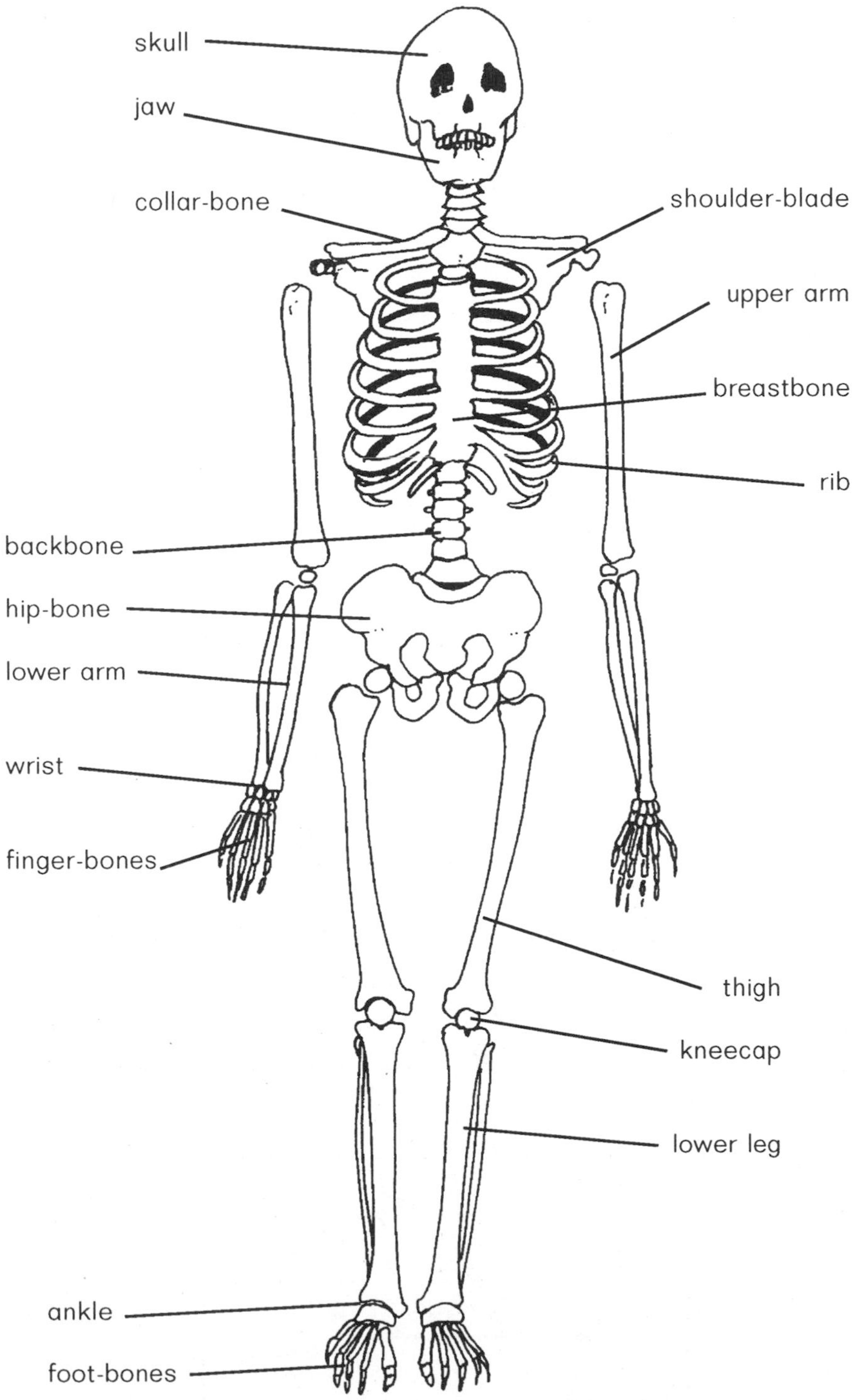

skull

jaw

collar-bone

shoulder-blade

upper arm

breastbone

rib

backbone

hip-bone

lower arm

wrist

finger-bones

thigh

kneecap

lower leg

ankle

foot-bones

distance around head

_____ cm

distance from base of
neck to top of arm

_____ cm

length of second finger

_____ cm

distance around wrist

_____ cm

length of lower arm
from elbow to wrist

_____ cm

length of upper arm
from shoulder to elbow

_____ cm

length of thigh
from hip to knee

_____ cm

length of lower leg
from knee to ankle

_____ cm

distance around ankle

_____ cm

length of foot from heel
to tip of big toe

_____ cm

LIFE PROCESSES
AND LIVING THINGS

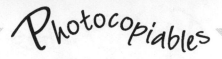

Our joints, see page 75

Our joints

Name _____   Date _____

▲ Name the joints and bones in the pictures using the list of words provided.

Word list

leg-bone
hinge joint
skull
arm
hip-bone
jaw
wrist
plane joint
ball and
socket joint

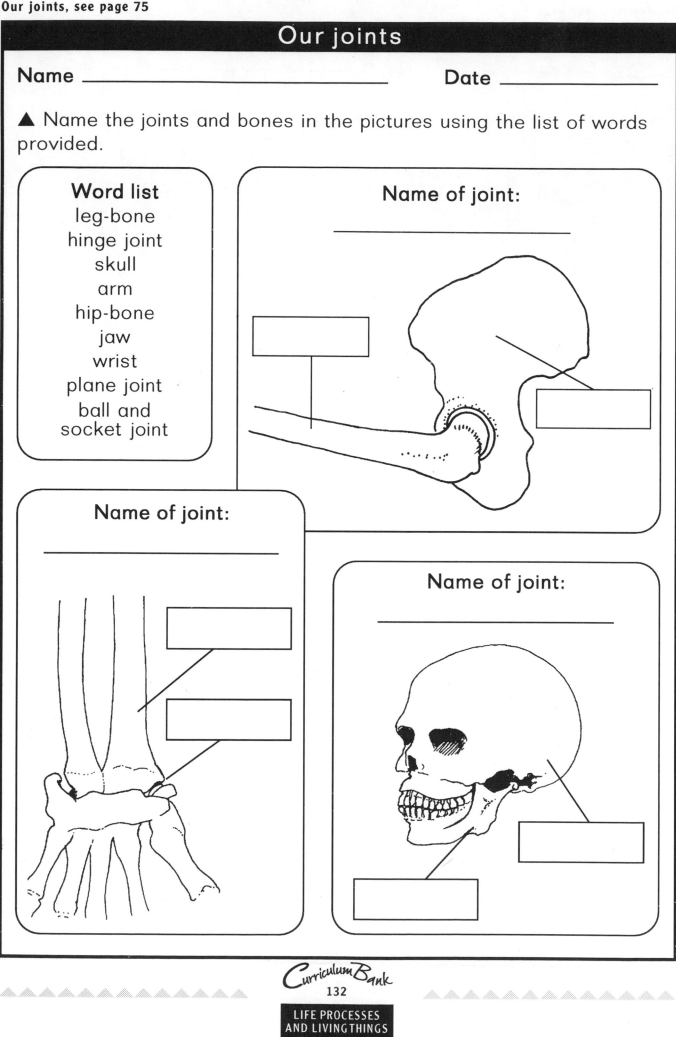

Name of joint:
_____

Name of joint:
_____

Name of joint:
_____

LIFE PROCESSES
AND LIVING THINGS

Muscles, see page 76

My muscles

Name _____

Date _____

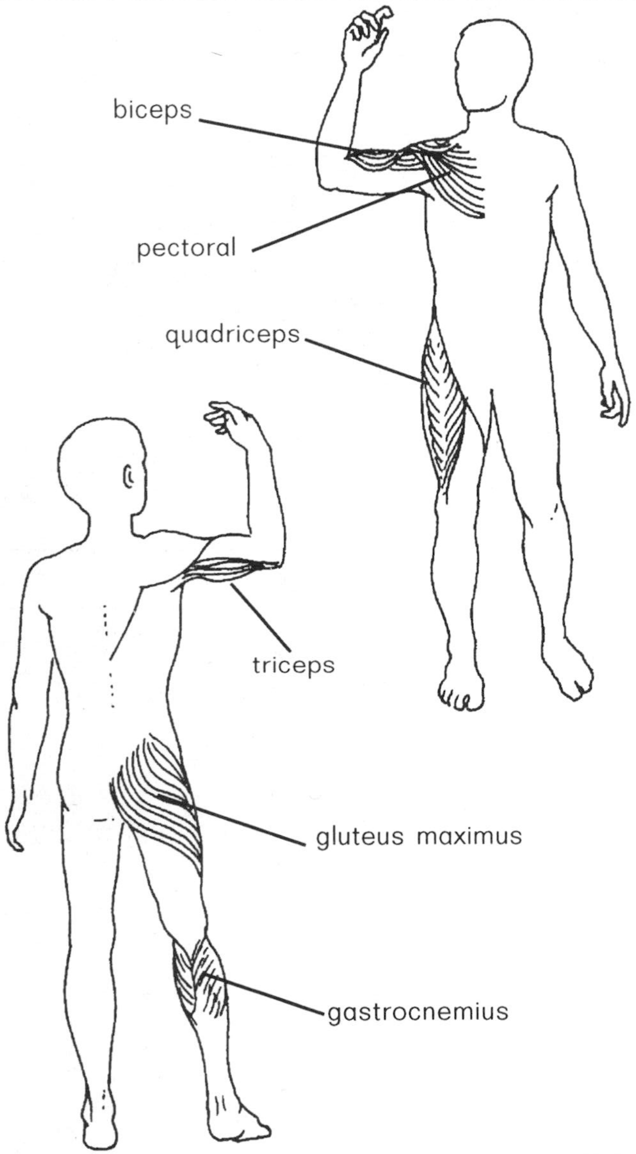

Measurement	Me	My partner
Around middle of upper arm when arm is straight.		
Around middle of upper arm when arm is bent and fist is clenched.		
Around middle of thigh when standing.		
Around middle of thigh when squatting.		
Around top of chest when shoulders are forward.		
Around top of chest when shoulders are back.		
Gripping bathroom scales with right hand.		
Gripping bathroom scales with left hand.		

biceps
pectoral
quadriceps
triceps
gluteus maximus
gastrocnemius

LIFE PROCESSES
AND LIVING THINGS

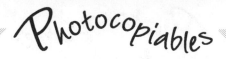
Our heart, see page 78

Make a model valve

Name _____   Date _____

You will need: a clear plastic bottle, stiff card, scissors, a craft knife, adhesive tape, a small weight (a battery or marble).

1. Cut the end off the bottle.
2. Cut a thin slit in the side of the bottle.

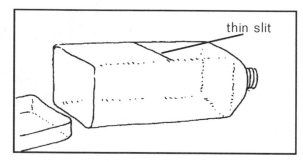

thin slit

3. Cut a strip of card as wide as the slit and about 3cm longer than the diameter of the bottle. Taper one end of the strip of card.
4. Push the card (tapered end first) into the slit until it touches the other side of the bottle.

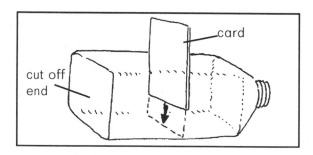

card

cut off end

5. Cut out a piece of card about 3cm long and 2cm wide to use as a card stopper. Bend it in half.
6. Cut a small slit in the bottle, just below where the tapered end of the piece of card is touching the side of the bottle.

7. Push the stopper into the small slit, so that the card strip is resting on the stopper. Secure the stopper in place on the outside of the bottle with adhesive tape.

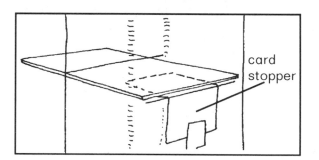

card stopper

8. Drop a weight through one end of the bottle. What happens? Now try the other end. What happens?

LIFE PROCESSES AND LIVING THINGS

Pulse rate, see page 79

Pulse rate

Name _____ Date _____

Does your pulse rate change with exercise?
▲ Work with a partner on this activity to find out.

You will need: a stopwatch or watch with a second hand, a skipping rope, a pencil.

1. Find your pulse. Count the number of beats in half a minute, then double it for one minute. Record your results in the chart below.
2. Touch your toes 20 times. Count your pulse beats for half a minute, then double the number. Record your results.
3. Jump up and down 50 times. Count your pulse beats for half a minute, then double the number. Record your results.
4. Skip for two minutes. Count your pulse beats for half a minute, then double the number. Record your results.

Results				
Name	Number of beats per minute			
	Rest	Touching toes	Jumping	Skipping

▲ Compare your results for different exercises. Why do you think your pulse rate changes after exercise?

LIFE PROCESSES AND LIVING THINGS

Exercise

Name _____   Date _____

How much exercise do you and your family do?

▲ Carry out this survey to find out.

▲ Answer the questions yourself, then ask two adults from your family.

Question	_____ (Name)	_____ (Name)	_____ (Name)
How many hours do you sit down at work/school in a day?			
How many hours do you watch TV each day?			
Do you walk to work/school each day?			
Do you walk a dog each day?			
Do you ride a bicycle each day?			
Do you ride a bicycle sometimes?			
Do you play a sport each week?			
Do you do training exercises for a sport each week?			
Do you go swimming each week?			
Do you climb stairs every day?			
Do you go for long walks each week?			
Do you do PE/fitness activities each week?			

▲ Discuss the survey answers with a friend. Do you think you do enough exercise each week?

LIFE PROCESSES AND LIVING THINGS

Smoking, see page 83

Smoking survey

Name _____   Date _____

▲ Ask two adults (one who smokes tobacco and one who does not) the following questions.

Questions for smoker

How old were you when you started smoking? _____

Why did you start smoking? _____

How many cigarettes do you smoke in a day? _____

Have you tried to give up? _____

What things have you tried to help you give up smoking? _____

_____

Does smoking affect your health? How? _____

_____

Would you encourage young people to smoke? Why/why not? _____

_____

Questions for non-smoker

Did you try smoking when you were younger? _____

Why did you decide not to smoke? _____

_____

Do you think cigarettes should be banned? _____

Should people be allowed to smoke in restaurants? _____

_____

Do you allow smoking in your house? _____

How would you discourage young people from smoking? _____

_____

LIFE PROCESSES
AND LIVING THINGS

Human life cycle, see page 85

The human life cycle

Name _____   Date _____

▲ Cut out the pictures below. Put them in the correct order to show all the stages of the human life cycle.

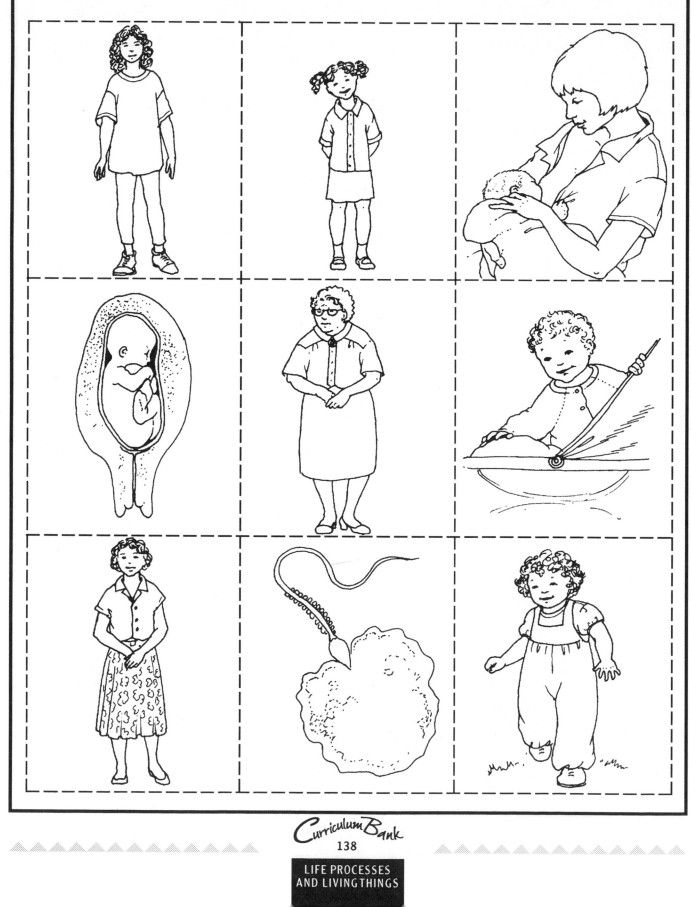

**LIFE PROCESSES
AND LIVING THINGS**

Assessment activities – Living and non-living things

1 ▲ Write down the names of these animals.

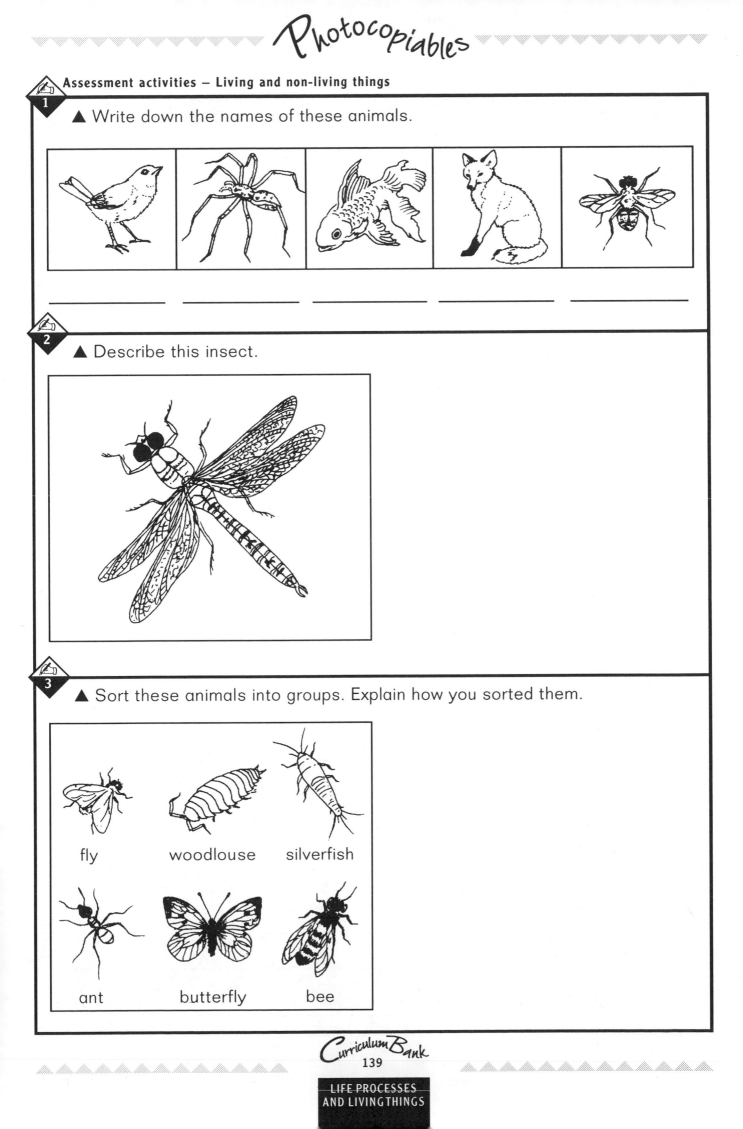

_____ _____ _____ _____ _____

2 ▲ Describe this insect.

3 ▲ Sort these animals into groups. Explain how you sorted them.

fly   woodlouse   silverfish

ant   butterfly   bee

Photocopiables

4

▲ Tick three things this kitten will need to grow and stay healthy.

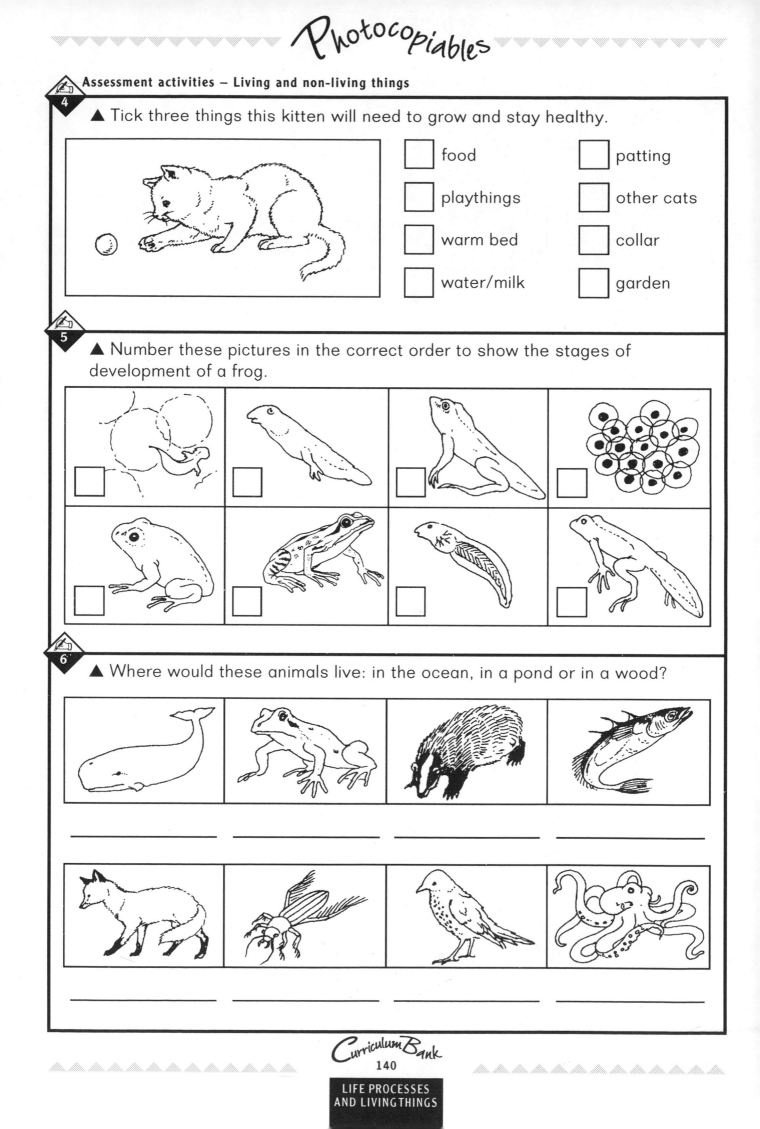

☐ food   ☐ patting

☐ playthings   ☐ other cats

☐ warm bed   ☐ collar

☐ water/milk   ☐ garden

5

▲ Number these pictures in the correct order to show the stages of development of a frog.

6

▲ Where would these animals live: in the ocean, in a pond or in a wood?

_____

_____

Assessment activities – Living and non-living things

7

▲ Which of these things are living? Tick the correct boxes.

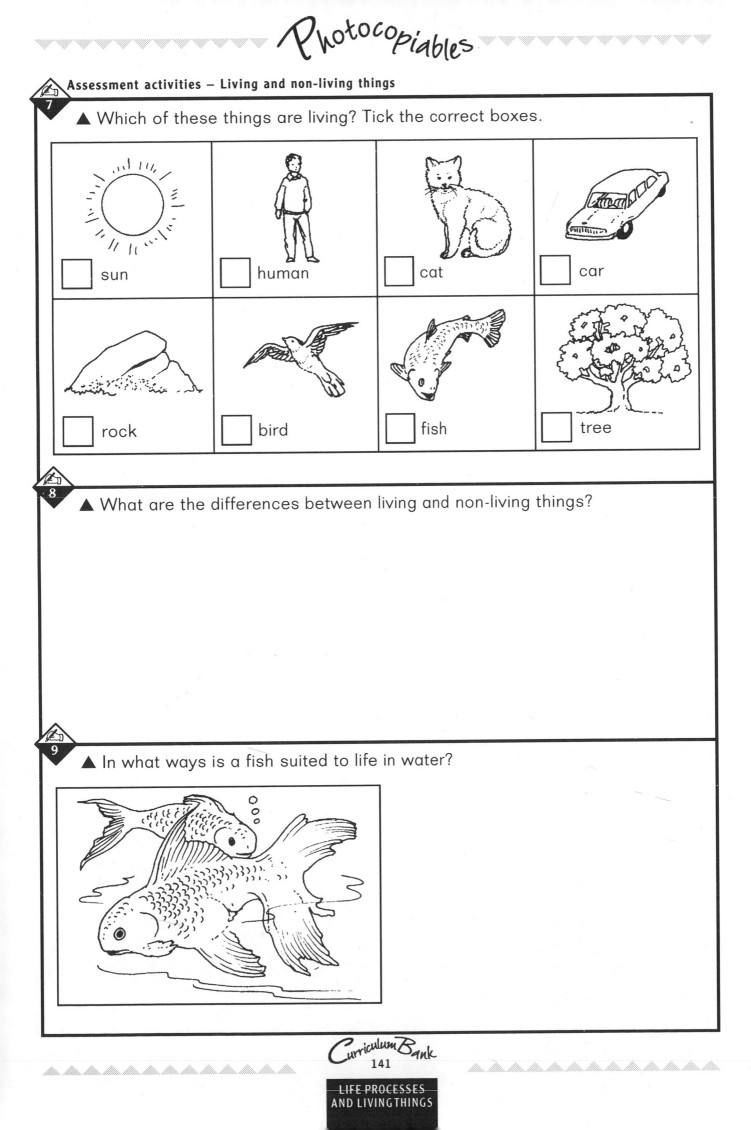

☐ sun

☐ human

☐ cat

☐ car

☐ rock

☐ bird

☐ fish

☐ tree

8

▲ What are the differences between living and non-living things?

9

▲ In what ways is a fish suited to life in water?

LIFE PROCESSES AND LIVING THINGS

Assessment activities – Living and non-living things

10

▲ What do all of these things have in common? Tick the boxes to show this.

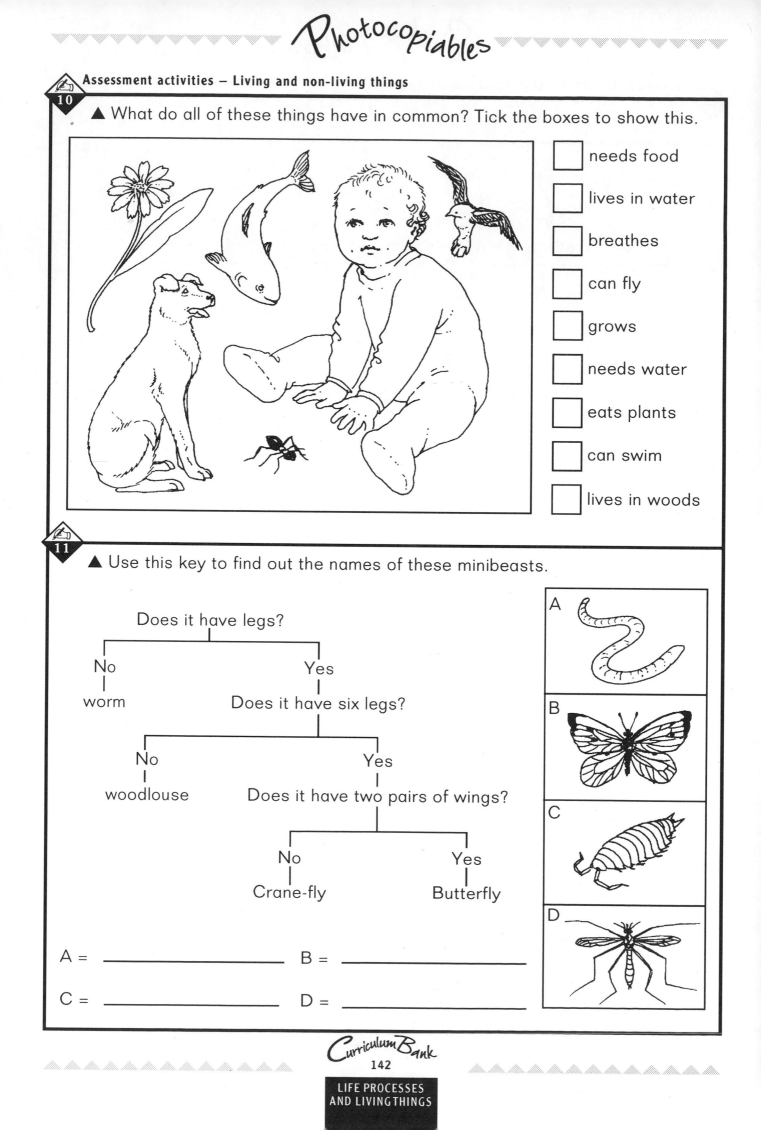

☐ needs food

☐ lives in water

☐ breathes

☐ can fly

☐ grows

☐ needs water

☐ eats plants

☐ can swim

☐ lives in woods

11

▲ Use this key to find out the names of these minibeasts.

Does it have legs?

No — worm

Yes
Does it have six legs?

No — woodlouse

Yes
Does it have two pairs of wings?

No
Crane-fly

Yes
Butterfly

A

B

C

D

A = _____   B = _____

C = _____   D = _____

12

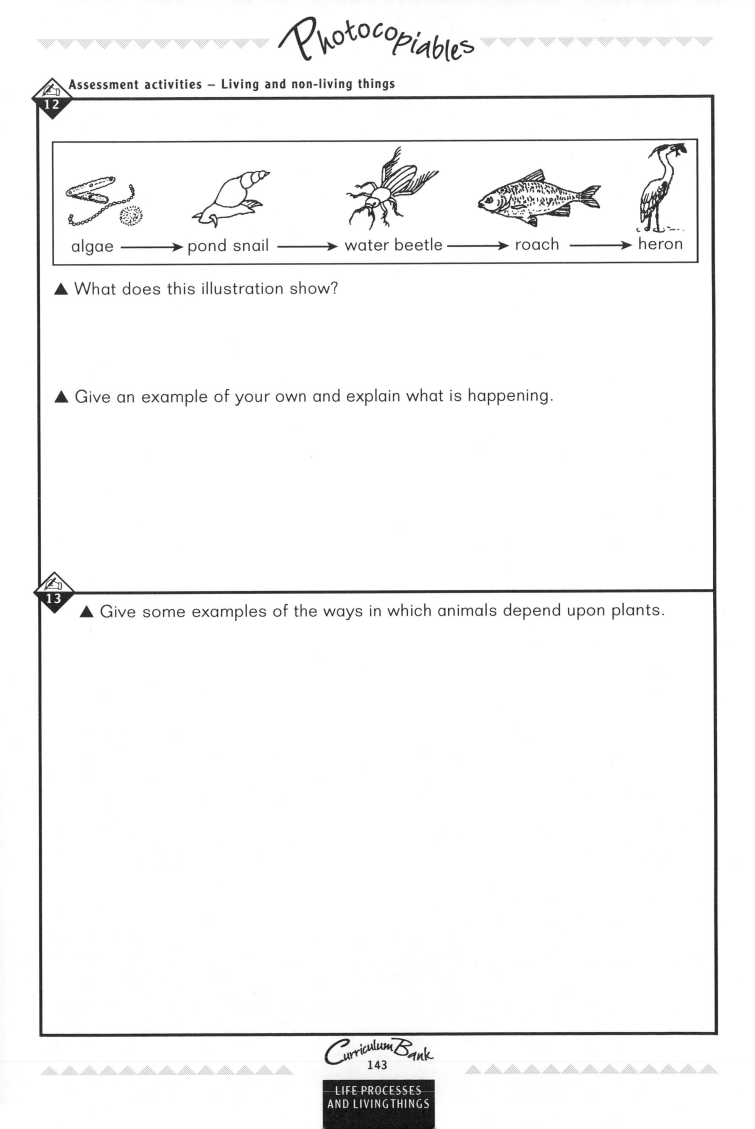

algae ⟶ pond snail ⟶ water beetle ⟶ roach ⟶ heron

▲ What does this illustration show?

▲ Give an example of your own and explain what is happening.

13

▲ Give some examples of the ways in which animals depend upon plants.

Assessment activities – Plants

1 ▲ Name these living things.

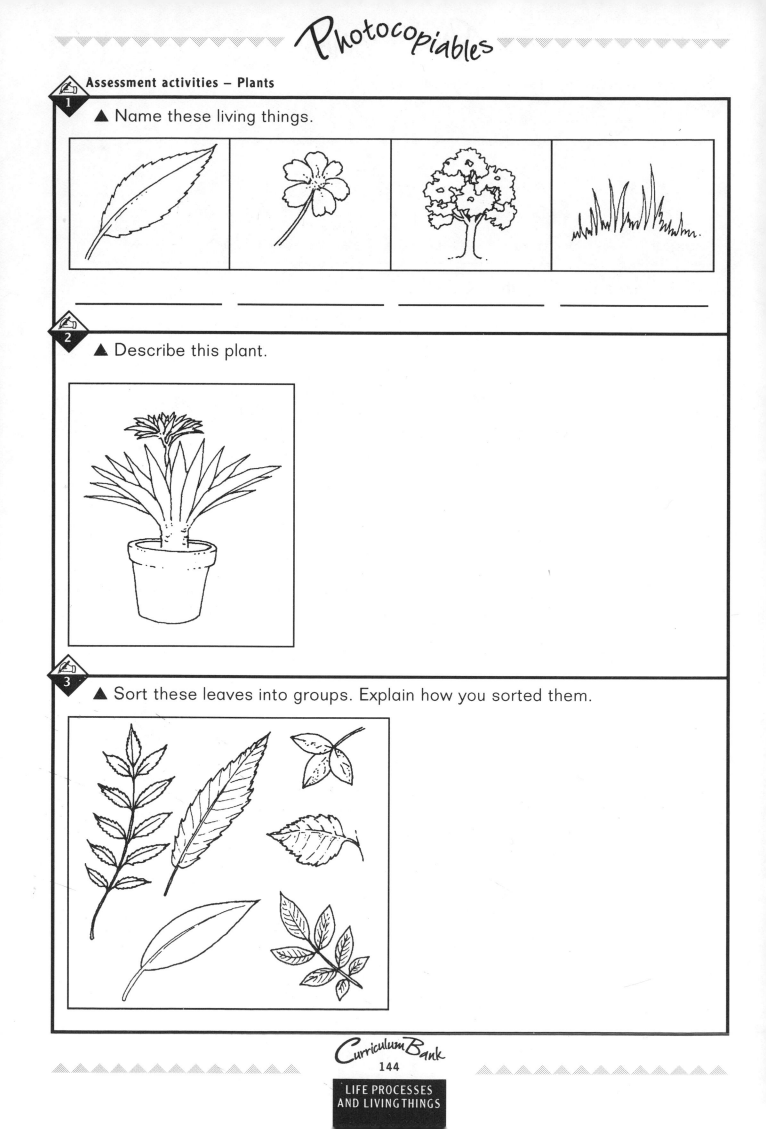

_____   _____   _____   _____

2 ▲ Describe this plant.

3 ▲ Sort these leaves into groups. Explain how you sorted them.

LIFE PROCESSES
AND LIVING THINGS

Assessment activities – Plants

4 ▲ Tick the plant(s) you think will grow well.

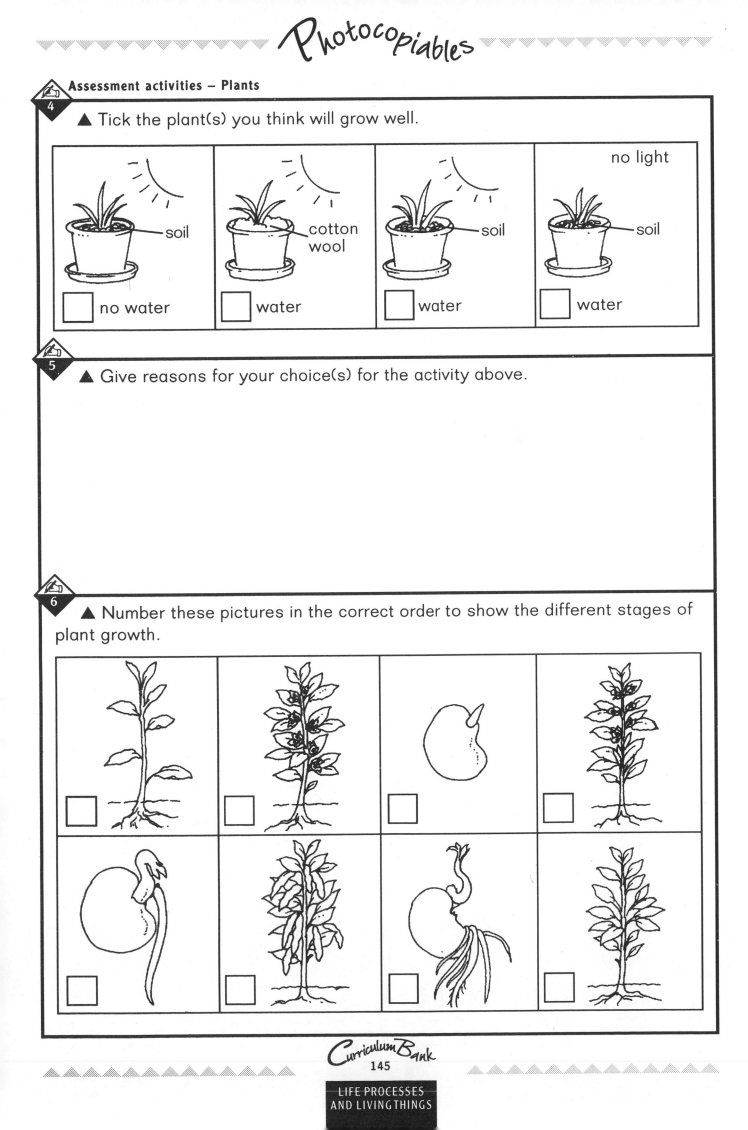

no light

soil

cotton wool

soil

soil

☐ no water ☐ water ☐ water ☐ water

5 ▲ Give reasons for your choice(s) for the activity above.

6 ▲ Number these pictures in the correct order to show the different stages of plant growth.

Assessment activities – Plants

7

▲ Where would these plants live? In a pond or a wood?

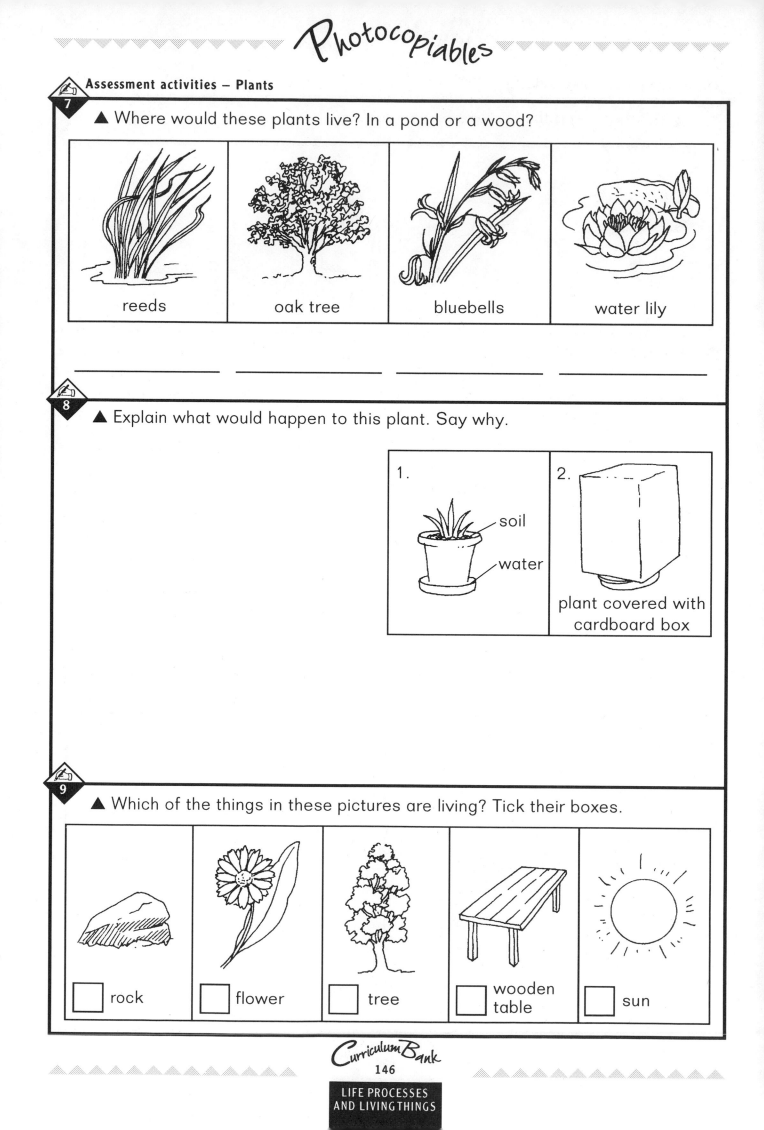

reeds	oak tree	bluebells	water lily

_____   _____   _____   _____

8

▲ Explain what would happen to this plant. Say why.

1.

soil

water

2.

plant covered with
cardboard box

9

▲ Which of the things in these pictures are living? Tick their boxes.

☐ rock	☐ flower	☐ tree	☐ wooden table	☐ sun

Assessment activities – Plants

10 ▲ What do living things have in common?

11 ▲ Label the parts of this plant.

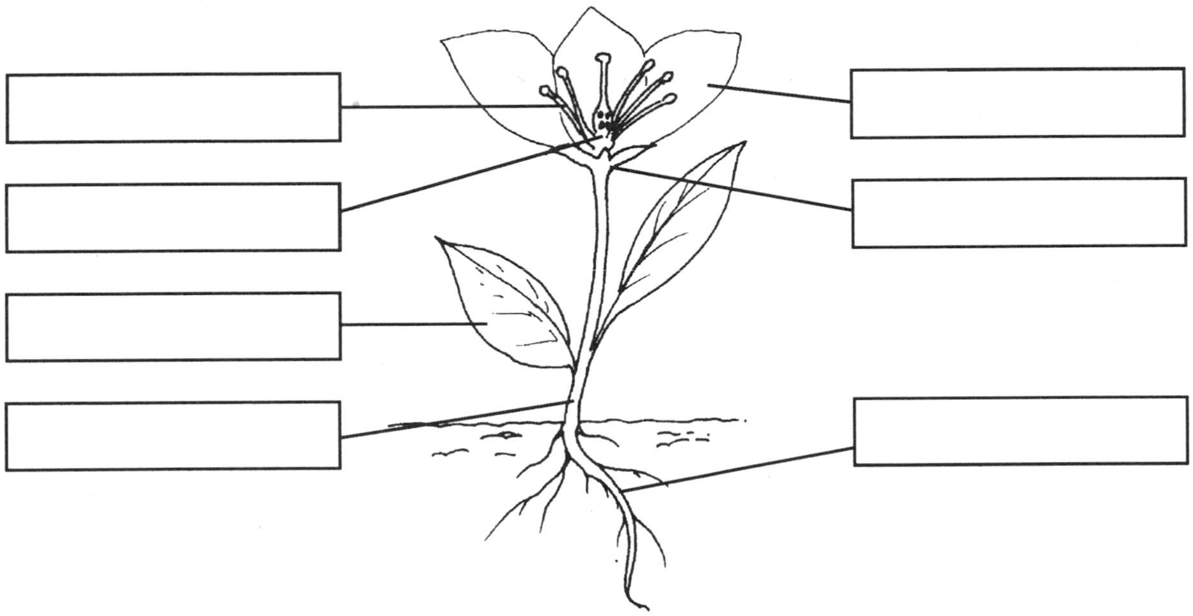

12 ▲ What do these plant parts do for the plant?

a) roots	b) stem
c) leaves	d) flowers

Assessment activities – Plants

13

▲ Look at the pictures. Use this key to find the names of the plants.

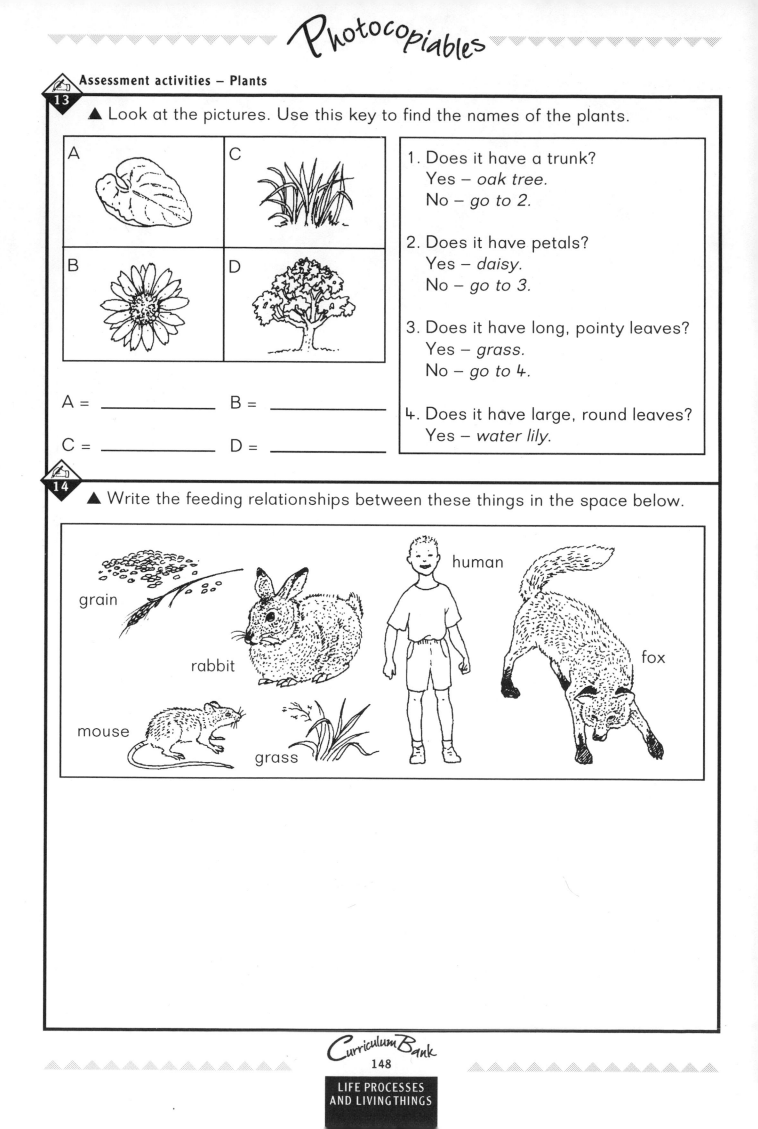

A

C

B

D

A = _____   B = _____

C = _____   D = _____

1. Does it have a trunk?
   Yes – *oak tree.*
   No – *go to 2.*

2. Does it have petals?
   Yes – *daisy.*
   No – *go to 3.*

3. Does it have long, pointy leaves?
   Yes – *grass.*
   No – *go to 4.*

4. Does it have large, round leaves?
   Yes – *water lily.*

14

▲ Write the feeding relationships between these things in the space below.

grain

rabbit

mouse

grass

human

fox

Assessment activities – Plants

15 ▲ Explain why plants are important to other living things.

16 ▲ Number these pictures in the correct order to show the life cycle of the dandelion.

17 ▲ What do these plant parts do for the plant?

a) petals

b) stigma

c) stamen

Assessment activities – Plants

18

▲ Describe the main stages in the life cycle of a flowering plant. How is it similar to the human life cycle?

19

▲ What features do these plants have which help them to survive in their habitats? Write your answers in the space below.

desert	wood	pond

a) cactus

b) tree

c) water lily

LIFE PROCESSES
AND LIVING THINGS

Assessment activities – Ourselves

1

▲ Label these body parts.

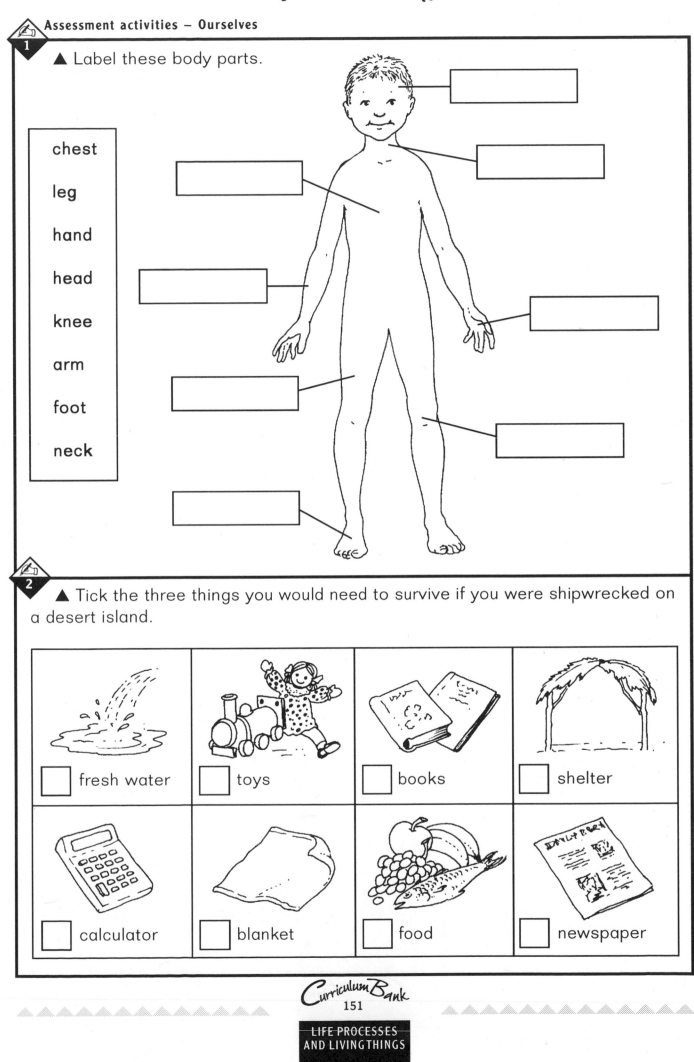

chest

leg

hand

head

knee

arm

foot

neck

2

▲ Tick the three things you would need to survive if you were shipwrecked on a desert island.

☐ fresh water	☐ toys	☐ books	☐ shelter
☐ calculator	☐ blanket	☐ food	☐ newspaper

LIFE PROCESSES
AND LIVING THINGS

Assessment activities – Ourselves

3 ▲ Number these pictures in the correct order to show how a human being grows and changes.

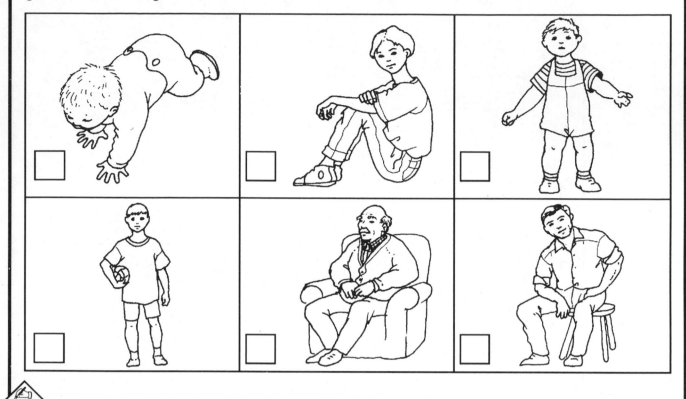

4 ▲ Sort these people into two groups. Write 1 or 2 next to each of them, to show who belongs in which group. Explain how you sorted them.

How I sorted them:

LIFE PROCESSES
AND LIVING THINGS

Photocopiables

5 ▲ Tick four things that humans have in common with other animals.

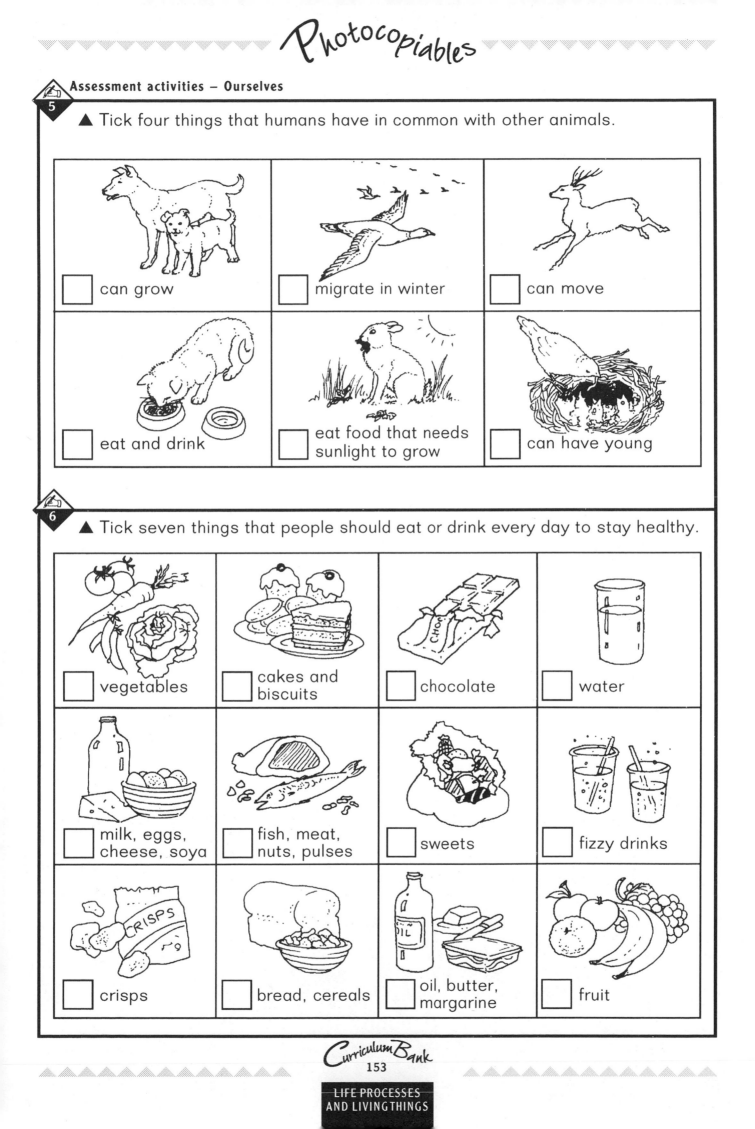

| can grow | migrate in winter | can move |
| eat and drink | eat food that needs sunlight to grow | can have young |

6 ▲ Tick seven things that people should eat or drink every day to stay healthy.

vegetables	cakes and biscuits	chocolate	water
milk, eggs, cheese, soya	fish, meat, nuts, pulses	sweets	fizzy drinks
crisps	bread, cereals	oil, butter, margarine	fruit

Assessment activities – Ourselves

7

▲ Describe how a poor diet could affect people's health.

▲ What things can you do to help yourself stay healthy?

8

▲ Write down three things you should do to care for your teeth.

▲ Why do we have teeth?

9

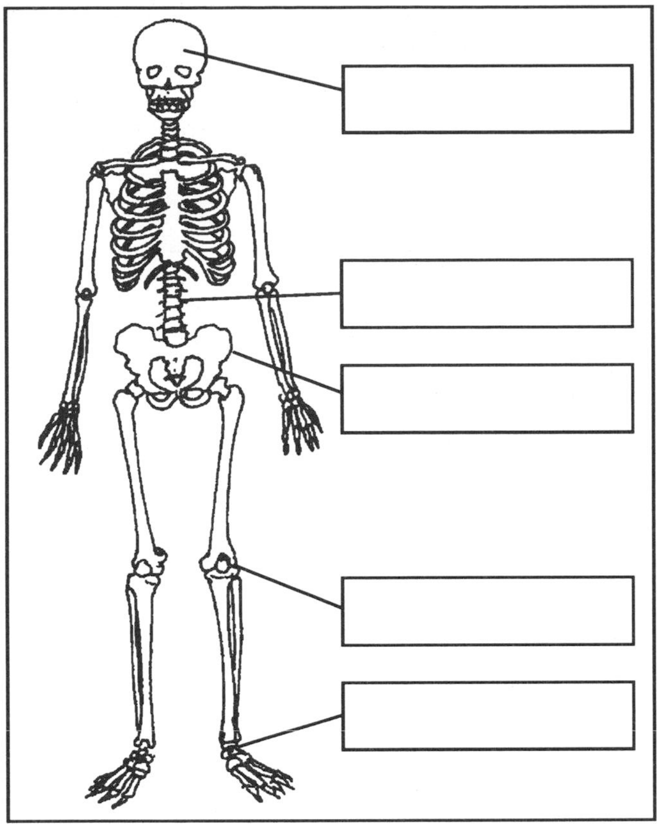

▲ Describe what our bones and muscles do.

Label these bones on the diagram:
**hip-bone   ankle   backbone
skull   kneecap**

10

▲ Name the body organ illustrated on the right.

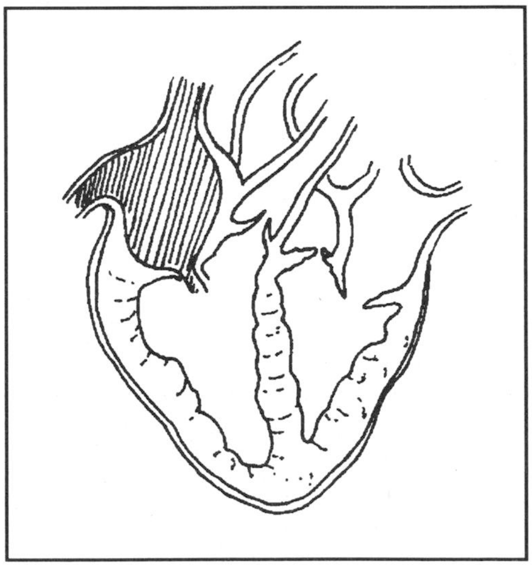

▲ What does it do?

▲ Why is it important?

▲ What do the arteries do?

Photocopiables

Assessment activities – Ourselves

11

▲ Look carefully at the chart below, then answer the three questions.

What were James and Sally investigating?

Name	Number of beats per minute		
	At rest	20 sit-ups	Running for 20 minutes
James	78	90	102
Sally	84	96	113

What do their results tell you?

Can you explain why?

12

▲ Which of these things could be harmful to your health if you took them?

☐ cigarettes   ☐ cough mixture   ☐ aspirin   ☐ heroin

☐ alcohol   ☐ inhaler   ☐ coffee   ☐ someone else's tablets

☐ antacid tablets   ☐ anti-depressants   ☐ sleeping tablets   ☐ sweets

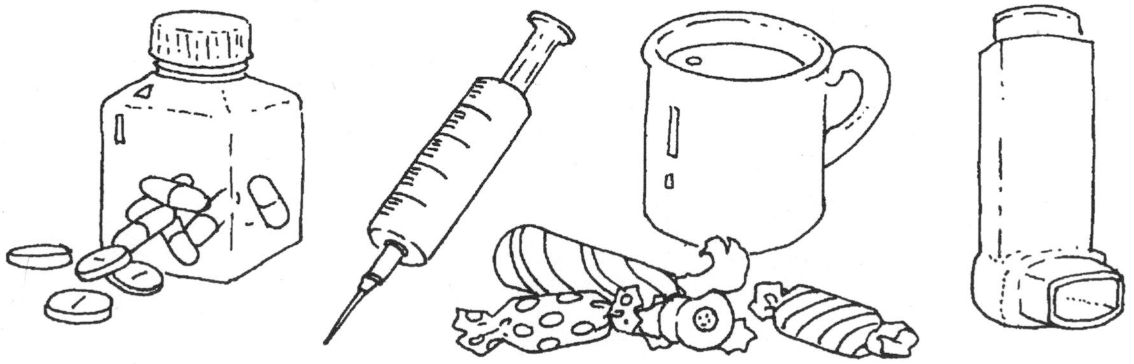

Curriculum Bank
156

LIFE PROCESSES AND LIVING THINGS

Photocopiables

13 ▲ Name the organs in this diagram.

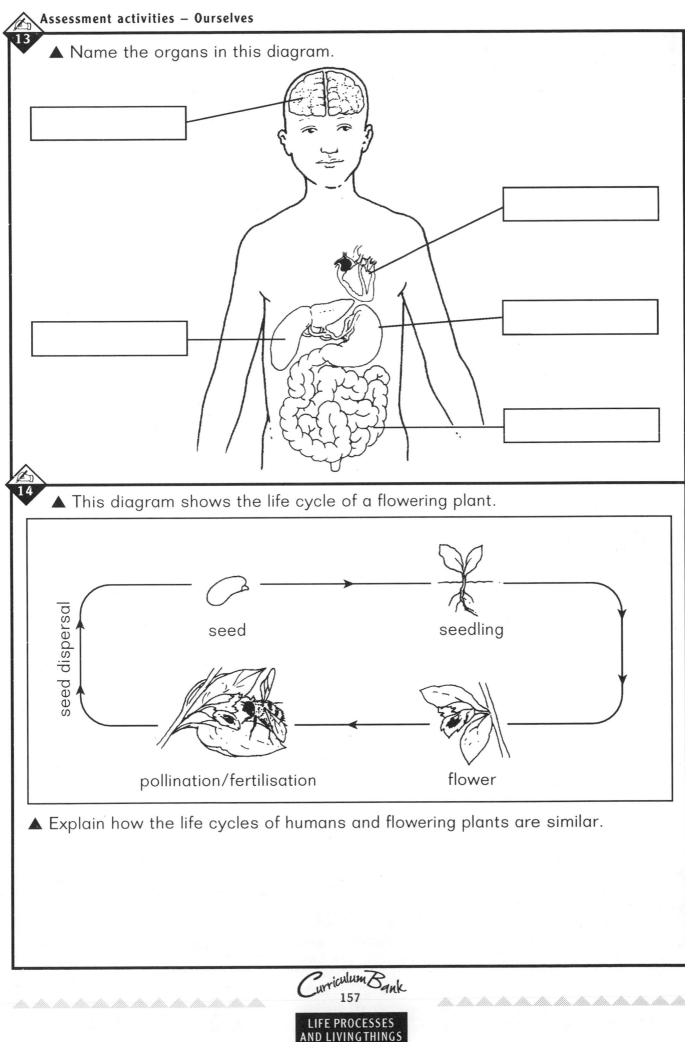

14 ▲ This diagram shows the life cycle of a flowering plant.

seed dispersal

seed

seedling

pollination/fertilisation

flower

▲ Explain how the life cycles of humans and flowering plants are similar.

LIFE PROCESSES
AND LIVING THINGS

INFORMATION TECHNOLOGY WITHIN SCIENCE

The main emphasis for the development of IT capability within the activities of this book is on information handling using databases, branching databases, spreadsheets and graphing software. There are also some activities where children might use electronic measurement or data-logging techniques using either the computer or hand-held measuring devices.

This brief outline looks at the key features of the main types of software used in the activities of this book, and gives some information for teachers about using them with children.

Databases

Although the simplest approach to the use of databases is for pupils to explore a database which has been made by someone else, it will not be long before pupils want to add their own information or create their own database. When children are involved in creating their own databases, it is important to discuss with them the need for a consistent approach to the collection of data. If children collect hair colours, for example, they may tend to use different words for the same colour (fair, blonde, white, yellow, and so on). Some time spent with the class as a whole looking at categories will save much wasted effort. If the children are going to combine their information into a class database, a common and consistent data collection sheet is essential.

It is also important to plan the work carefully to ensure that once the database has been completed, there is time for the children to use it in a meaningful way. Try to plan database activities across several weeks. An initial lesson could start the data collection; data entry could take place over the next few weeks; and then a return to the topic could stimulate questions and ideas for the children to try out with the completed database. Where possible, try to relate the children's database to those used in the wider world and to issues such as the accuracy and privacy of information stored on such systems.

Branching databases

These types of database are useful for helping children to develop sorting and classifying skills; they are an electronic version of the traditional paper key. The children give the computer information about a set of items so that the computer can then guide someone else to identify an object from the known set. Branching databases are excellent for developing language skills, as all questions have to result in 'Yes' or 'No' answers. Some preliminary work in phrasing this type of question needs to be done before starting to use the software. Children benefit from working in groups to create a branching database. As the first questions are usually vital to the success of the database, some preliminary work away from the computer is a good idea. The database can usually be saved so that the children can come back to it at a later date.

Spreadsheets

Much of the data collection done in science work lends itself to a tabular format. Spreadsheets are an ideal way of recording such information. When a class is working on an investigation, it is possible for the children to record their measurements directly on to a class or group spreadsheet. It is then easy to print out a copy for the whole class or for each group. The tabular format allows the children to see all of the data at one go, without having to search across a database. Initially it will be easier for the teacher to set up the spreadsheet, particularly when there are formulae to be used. However, as time goes by the children can begin to develop their own spreadsheets.

Most spreadsheets now have graphing facilities which allow children to draw a range of graphs, such as line graphs, bar graphs, pie charts and scattergrams. If the information is recorded on a single spreadsheet, graphs can be drawn of those parts of the information that are needed. Some spreadsheets even allow graphics to be used for pictograms.

The other advantage of spreadsheets for data collection is that simple formulae can be set into the spreadsheet. For example, averages or totals for a class data set can easily be calculated. Where children take several measurements of the same event, the spreadsheet can automatically calculate the average of the measurements taken. It is also possible to sort information numerically and alphabetically.

Graphing software

A range of software is available which allows children to record their information on to the computer and then to draw a range of graphs. This does not require the setting up of spreadsheets to begin with, and can be particularly useful for exploring patterns. The computer allows the children to concentrate on interpreting the data they have collected, rather than on the task of drawing graphs. Children can also explore a range of different graphs, usually bar charts, line graphs, pie charts and scattergrams, and make decisions about the most appropriate type of graph for the information they want to display.

Software grids

The grids on the facing page relate the activities in this book to specific areas of IT and to relevant software resources. Activities are referenced by page number rather than by name. (Bold page numbers indicate activities which have expanded IT content.) The software listed on the second grid is a selection of programs generally available to primary schools, and is not intended as a recommended list. The software featured should be available from most good educational software retailers.

IT links

AREA OF IT	TYPE OF SOFTWARE	ACTIVITIES (page nos.)		
		CHAPTER 1	**CHAPTER 2**	**CHAPTER 3**
Communicating Information	Word Processor	26, 28, 33	45, 50, 51, 56, 58, 61	70, 72, 75, 78, 84
Communicating Information	DTP	28, 31	45	
Communicating Information	Art/graphics	26, 34	49	72
Communicating Information	Multimedia authoring	28	**61**	
Communicating/ Handling Information	Graphing software		40, **44**, 45, 49, 50	64, 71
Information Handling	Database	16, 18, 21, 28		**65**, 68, 71, 79, 81, 83
Information Handling	Branching database	14, **24**, 26	41, 42	
Information Handling	Spreadsheet		**44**, 45, 47, 49	67, 71, 74, 76, 79
Information Handling	CD-ROM	15, 28, 31	**61**	78
Measuring	Data sensing		49	79

SOFTWARE TYPE	BBC/MASTER	RISCOS	NIMBUS/186	WINDOWS	MACINTOSH
Word Processor	Pendown	Pendown 2 Folio Impression Style	Write On Caxton	Claris Works Creative Writer Word	Claris Works Word Word Writer's Toolkit
DTP	Typesetter	Desktop Folio Impression Style Ovation First Page	Newspaper Caxton Press	Microsoft Publisher	Kid Pix Fine Artist
Art Package	Image	1st Paint ProArtisan Revelation	Paintspa Plus	Colour Magic Kid Pix	
Multimedia Authoring		Magpie Genesis Key Author		MMBox2 Genesis	Hyperstudio
Database	Grass	Junior Pinpoint Keynote Find IT Bodymapper	Grass Sparks	Claris Works Junior Pinpoint Information Workshop Bodymapper	Claris Works Bodymapper
Branching Database	Branch	Retreeval	Branch		
Spreadsheet	Grasshopper	Grasshopper Data Suite Data Graph Advantage	Grasshopper	Claris Works Starting Grids Easy Works	Claris Works Easy Works
Graphing Software	Data Show	Graph IT Data Plot Data Graph		Data Plot Claris Works	Claris Works

LIFE PROCESSES
AND LIVING THINGS

	ENGLISH	MATHS	HISTORY	GEOGRAPHY	D&T	IT	ART	MUSIC	RE
LIVING THINGS AND THEIR ENVIRONMENT	Discussions about how humans and animals can affect the environment. Writing about local environmental issues. Making an ABC of animals. Debate – killing animals is wrong. Stories about animals.	Shapes, patterns in nature. Fibonacci numbers. Surveys of favourite animals – graphing results.	How animals have helped humans throughout time. Local history: how landscape affects settlement.	How people affect the environment – pollution, conservation. River studies. Animals and plants in local and other places.	Design ideal animal homes for animals from different environments. Design a poster showing how humans can protect the environment. Design your own animal.	Using a database program to store and retrieve information about animals and their habitats.	Animals in art. Landscapes. Observational drawings of animals. Clay models of animals.	Making up raps and songs about caring for our world. Listening to songs about animals.	Animal stories from the Bible – Noah's Ark, Samson. Caring for living things. Protecting our world. Religion and animals – sacred animals, Jewish diet, stories of creation.
PLANTS	Making an ABC of plants. Discussion about how plants help us. Stories about plants. Dramatise 'Jack and the Beanstalk'.	Shapes, area, perimeter of leaves. Measuring height of trees. Measuring growth rate of plants. Symmetry in leaves. Estimation – number of seeds in a packet.	Use of papyrus in Ancient Egypt. Local history – food and farming aspects.	How weather affects plant growth. Comparing plants and crops in the local area with another place.	Design an 'ideal home' for a plant. Make a model flower. Make a poster showing how to care for plants. Design your own plant. Design a garden for home or school.	Using a database program to store and retrieve information about local plants.	Plants in art. Observational drawings of plants. Collages using seeds. Leaf rubbings. Printing using plant parts.	Instruments made from plants – wood, rice, gourds. Making music to represent plants growing from seed.	Bible stories – parable of the sower, Moses in the bulrushes, Garden of Eden. Use of plants in religious ceremonies.
OURSELVES	Talking about ourselves and our families. Writing about ourselves – hobbies, interests, favourite things. Using pictures to discuss social issues. Writing poems about ourselves.	Measuring body parts, height, weight – graphing results. Area and perimeter of hands and feet.	History of medicines – breakthroughs to help fight disease. Social reforms. Lives of famous people. Victorian home life. Britain since 1930 – social aspects. Everyday life in Ancient Greece.	The effects of settlements on landscape. Comparing life in the local area to another place.	Design a symbol which means 'danger to health'. Design a poster about staying healthy. Consider the design of child-proof containers. Cooking healthy foods.	Using a database program to store and retrieve information about ourselves.	Human portraits in art. Observational drawings of people. Silhouettes of heads. Self-portraits.	Making up songs and raps about ourselves. Learning songs about ourselves.	Child protection – looking after ourselves and others. 'Friends' and 'strangers'. Our religious beliefs. Respecting other people's beliefs. Festivals, celebrations.